Sizing Water Service Lines and Meters

Third Edition

**American Water Works
Association**

Manual of Water Supply Practices—M22, Third Edition

Sizing Water Service Lines and Meters

If you find errors in this manual, please email books@awwa.org. Possible errata will be posted at www.awwa.org/resources-tools/resource-development-groups/manuals-program.aspx.

Project Manager/Senior Technical Editor: Melissa Valentine
Senior Manuals Specialist: Molly Beach
Senior Production Editor: Cheryl Armstrong

Library of Congress Cataloging-in-Publication Data
Sizing water service lines and meters / [editors] Peter W. Mayer, Colleen M. Arnold, Bradford P. Brainard.
    -- Third edition.
      pages cm. -- (Manual of water supply practices ; M22)
    Includes bibliographical references and index.
    ISBN 978-1-62576-027-2 (alk. paper) -- ISBN 978-1-61300-286-5 (eISBN) 1. Water consumption--Measurement. 2. Water-pipes. 3. Water-meters. 4. Water--Distribution--Planning. I. Mayer, Peter W., editor. II. Arnold, Colleen M., editor. III. Brainard, Bradford P., editor. IV. American Water Works Association.
    TD499.S59 2014
    628.1'44--dc23
                2014028029

Printed in the United States of America

ISBN: 978-1-62576-027-2   eISBN: 978-1-61300-286-5

American Water Works Association

American Water Works Association
6666 West Quincy Avenue
Denver, CO 80235-3098
awwa.org

Contents

Figures

This page intentionally blank.

Tables

Preface

The American Water Works Association published the first edition of M22, *Sizing Water Service Lines and Meters*, in 1975. The manual was the first effort to provide guidance to the water industry on sizing water meters and services to meet the objectives of water utilities and their customers. The AWWA Distribution and Plant Operations Division recognized that the manual was in need of an update to incorporate changes in water demands that have occurred over the past 10 years and to offer a method for sizing dedicated irrigation meters that aligns with practices used by the Irrigation Association. In 1995, a manual revision subcommittee was established to review the existing manual and begin the process of developing an updated version and incorporating the impacts of existing technology into this sizing process. The efforts of that subcommittee resulted in the second edition (2004) of the meter and service-line sizing manual. In 2010, the Customer Metering Practices Committee formed a subcommittee to begin work on the third edition (2014) of M22. The subcommittee met regularly over a three-year period to complete the most recent update.

This manual provides guidance on sizing water meters and service lines to meet the objectives of water utilities and their customers. The information in this manual can be used to estimate customer demand and maximum expected flow at a site, and this can be used to appropriately size a new service line and meter. This manual includes a useful field method called *demand profiling* that can be used to evaluate actual customer use patterns and help optimize meter size selection.

The data presented in the manual were obtained using a variety of methods including: field measurements, utility surveys, technical publications, and hydraulic design calculations. This information has been condensed into a simplified format to assist readers in addressing most common service conditions. However, water and building systems are unique, and there may be complex meter and service sizing situations that are beyond the scope of this manual.

This page intentionally blank.

Acknowledgments

The members of the M22 subcommittee who were involved with updating the third edition of M22 include:

Chair, Peter W. Mayer, Water Demand Management, Boulder, Colo.

Colleen M. Arnold, Aqua America, Bryn Mawr, Pa.
Bradford P. Brainard, Master Meter Inc., Hinesburg, Vt.
Steven G. Buchberger, University of Cincinnati, Cincinnati, Ohio
Andrew Chastain-Howley, Black & Veatch, Arlington, Texas
Daniel P. Cole, IAPMO, Mokena, Ill.
Stephen E. Davis, ARCADIS, Phoenix, Ariz.
George H. DeJarlais, Badger Meter, Milwaukee, Wis.
Craig C. Hannah, Johnson Controls Inc., Lubbock, Texas
Neil D. Kaufman, Truckee Donner Public Utility District, Truckee, Calif.
George A. Kunkel Jr., Philadelphia Water Department, Philadelphia, Pa.
Frank S. Kurtz, American Water Works Association, Denver, Colo.
Arnold Strasser, Denver Water, Denver, Colo.
Matt A. Thomas, Mueller Systems, Cornelius, N.C.
Gary B. Trachtman, ARCADIS, Birmingham, Ala.
Tom Walski, Bentley Systems Inc., Nanticoke, Pa.
Karl Wiegand, Globe Fire Sprinkler Corporation, Standish, Mich.

This manual was approved by the Customer Metering Practices Committee. The membership at the time of approval was:

Chair, Stephen E. Davis, ARCADIS, Phoenix, Ariz.

Colleen M. Arnold, Aqua America, Bryn Mawr, Pa.
Bradford P. Brainard, Master Meter Inc., Hinesburg, Vt.
Chris Carey, Western Virginia Water Authority, Roanoke, Va.
Andrew Chastain-Howley, Black & Veatch, Arlington, Texas
Daniel P. Cole, IAPMO, Mokena, Ill.
Melissa Dame, SAIC, Laveen, Ariz.
Stephen E. Davis, ARCADIS, Phoenix, Ariz.
George H. DeJarlais, Badger Meter, Milwaukee, Wis.
James E. Fisher, Echologics, Erlanger, Ky.
Craig C. Hannah, Johnson Controls Inc., Lubbock, Texas
Patrick A. Hayes, Mammoth Community Water District, Mammoth Lakes, Calif.
Neil D. Kaufman, Truckee Donner Public Utility District, Truckee, Calif.
George A. Kunkel Jr., Philadelphia Water Department, Philadelphia, Pa.
Peter W. Mayer, Water Demand Management, Boulder, Colo.
John F. Sliwa, Alaimo Group, Sicklerville, N.J.
Arnold Strasser, Denver Water, Denver, Colo.
Reinhard Sturm, Water Systems Optimization Inc., San Francisco, Calif.
Scott Swanson, Sensus Metering Systems, Uniontown, Pa.
Brian A. Tegeler, San Antonio Water System, San Antonio, Texas

Matt A. Thomas, Mueller Systems, Cornelius, N.C.

Gary B. Trachtman, ARCADIS, Birmingham, Ala.

Karl Wiegand, Globe Fire Sprinkler Corporation, Standish, Mich.

Chapter **1**

Introduction

OVERVIEW

This is the third edition of AWWA Manual M22, *Sizing Water Service Lines and Meters*. The first edition was printed in 1975, and the second edition was printed in 2004. This new edition expands the ways to approach the sizing of water service lines and meters and offers improved methods for the sizing of dedicated irrigation meters.

M22 TARGET AUDIENCE

This manual is intended for use by
- Water utility managers
- Engineers
- Planners
- Technicians and field operations personnel
- Consultants involved with designing and constructing projects requiring water service
- Academicians

UPDATES

When the first edition (1975) of M22 was written, the primary guideline for projecting water demands was the fixture value method, which conservatively projected water demands based on then-existing fixtures and appliances. This method emphasized identifying the worst-case instantaneous peak demand that could occur for a given water account. In the last 40 years, fixtures, appliances, irrigation demands, and their implications for both meter and service-line sizing have changed drastically. The second edition (2004) of M22 included methods for developing locally specific demand profiles to enable meters and service lines to be sized based on current, local conditions that reflect changes in water use patterns that have occurred. This third edition (2014) expands on the 2004 approach and provides recommendations for future research that will systematically evaluate water demands for the purpose of more accurate meter sizing. A summary of the changes and recommendations is presented in the following sections for consideration in using Manual M22.

Summary of Content

This edition of M22 focuses on how to identify water demand patterns to accurately measure real demands and provides necessary information for final meter and line sizing decisions. Fortunately, water utilities seeking to right-size meters and service lines need not rely on old and potentially inaccurate data and methods. This manual emphasizes that utilities having more information about a specific sizing situation will result in the best sizing decision from the tap to the meter. The authors recognize that the water utilities and professionals who may be using this manual have varying degrees of familiarity regarding their local water demand patterns and peak demand profiles. This document is structured to encourage water utilities and water professionals to study and understand their own local water demands, to provide methods to identify real-time peak-demand requirements, and, with this knowledge, to approach sizing decisions and policies with adequate and current information.

The manual concludes with guidelines and tools for making meter and service-line sizing decisions. The manual also includes techniques for sizing both new meters and existing meters, which may need to be resized because of changing conditions or initial sizing decisions. These techniques may differ in particular for existing meters where accurate, real-time demand flow profile data can be collected to enhance meter sizing decisions.

Chapter 2: Consumer Water Demands, Trends, and Considerations

The manual is structured to establish water demand as the fundamental factor to consider when sizing water service lines and meters. Currently, more is known and understood about general water demand patterns and peak demands because of the increasing focus on demand management in the water industry. Many water demand studies have been conducted in recent years that indicate distinctly different water demand patterns between and among various user classes, land uses, and geographic regions. For example, peak demands can vary greatly depending on the regional location (e.g., semi-arid West versus the more temperate Northeast) and seasonal variation of a particular location. Some water service areas contain several microclimates, which may impact sizing decisions.

This chapter introduces a sampling of typical demand patterns in different utilities. Each water utility is encouraged to study its own customer water-use patterns to reflect any regional or local conditions that may influence sizing decisions or policies in its area. Water professionals will benefit from comparing sizing policies and decisions between water utilities with similar climates or service characteristics.

Chapter 3: Demand Profiling for Optimal Meter Sizing

In addition to better understanding general water demand patterns in a particular locale, measuring real-time peak demands may be an option when sizing both water service lines and meters. Chapter 3 reviews equipment and technology that are available to help water utilities and their constituencies better understand typical peak demand patterns and how water is used in their systems. The chapter also reviews how demand measurement equipment measures real-time peak demands and outlines general guidelines for using this equipment for meter sizing purposes. Several hundred utilities actively collect and use demand profile information to improve sizing decisions. Many water utilities have used demand profile information to downsize meters, reduce nonrevenue water, and bill for service more equitably in their water system. More equitable billing is achieved by right-sizing a higher percentage of meters so that water charges more accurately reflect water used. Current technology is helping water professionals to better understand the water demand conditions that are embedded in sizing decisions.

Chapter 4: Estimating Demands Using Fixture Values

To properly size water taps, meters, and service lines, the peak demands must be known for any specific tap. Chapter 4 reviews the best available methods. The fixture value method is still useful in cases in which demand profile data are not available or applicable. The method proposed in this chapter uses the first and second edition M22 tables and graphs but includes more current fixture values based on an operating pressure of 60 psi (414 kPa). The Distribution and Plant Operations Division members of AWWA have been collecting empirical measurements to generate a family of demand curves to replace the demand curves generated by Hunter's fixture unit approach. Both approaches are described in chapter 4 along with a method for sizing dedicated irrigation meters based on flow velocity limits recommended by the Irrigation Association.

Chapter 5: Service-Line Sizing

There is a distinction between service-line sizing decisions and meter sizing decisions. Service lines must be able to meet the instantaneous peak demand of a particular account and any possible successor account, preferably without impacting the level of water service to the customer. Meter sizing must primarily consider the accurate measurement for all expected flow ranges for the current account to ensure accurate billing of consumption. The difference is that the service line should be more conservatively sized in general (as local conditions warrant).

This chapter provides the framework for local water utilities to ensure service lines are sized to meet peak demands while considering all relevant factors, including system pressure, line size, material, head loss, elevation changes, and type of use. Sample calculations are included as a guideline to assist the users in their own calculations. Pipe flow friction loss tables are also included in appendix B.

Chapter 6: Meter Sizing

This chapter provides an overview of meter sizing criteria that could be considered in the sizing decision. The meter sizing process is discussed and outlined to ensure a thorough evaluation. Sample calculations are introduced for the fixture value method and for using real-time peak-demand profile data and are included as a guideline for engineers and others to use for local sizing decisions. Properly collected demand profile data can be an effective tool to size existing meters for specific conditions, but the fixture value method is often the best approach for new services.

Considerations When Sizing Water Meters and Service Lines

The following changes highlight the need to continually improve and update sizing methods.

Changes in Technology

Current water meters are technological products with high-tech reading capabilities. Technology exists to collect real-time water demand data (demand profiling). Technological changes have resulted in a more accurate characterization of actual water demand patterns by various user classes than was previously possible using fixture counts or monthly meter readings. Utilities can leverage these technological changes to customize meter and service line sizing based on relevant local information.

Demand Pattern Changes

Demand management has been institutionalized through national energy and water efficiency standards and codes and wider acceptance of water use efficiency. The result is that overall demands have decreased below those assumed in the fixture value method, and it is necessary to revise the fixture value method using modern data sets. This is an essential task that should be completed before the next update of this manual.

Policy Changes in Water Rate and Connection Fees

Water rate charges and connection fees are based on the meter size and service line size. As a result, sizing decisions are critical, and life-cycle cost and benefit implications from both the utility and customer perspective have heightened relevance.

Some utilities have separated meter sizing from the connection fee process. These utilities use demand-based approaches to connection fees and infrastructure charges for new customers. These approaches are independent of the meter and service line size and enable the utility and customer to focus on the expected annual demands at the site rather than the peak instantaneous demands needed for meter sizing.

Additionally, some combined water, wastewater, and stormwater utilities have removed the stormwater charge from the base, or fixed, charge in order to bill properties in a tailored fashion based on their land characteristics or stormwater management practices. Thus, the fixed charge based on meter size has decreased in these utilities. This trend may have an additional benefit in the case of oversized meters. Historically, some utilities lacked motivation to downsize oversized meters to obtain better low-flow accuracy because a higher fixed charge could be obtained from the larger meter. With a smaller fixed charge based on meter size, water utilities may be motivated to replace oversized meters with an optimally sized meter.

Growing Use of Residential Fire Sprinkler Systems

Jurisdictions have long had the opportunity to adopt requirements for residential fire sprinkler systems as prescribed under the National Fire Protection Association (NFPA) 13D Standard. While hundreds of local jurisdictions in the United States have done just that, the inclusion of a residential fire sprinkler requirement under the NFPA 13D Standard in the International Residential Code in 2009 spurred state-level requirements to implement these systems in the United States. Thus, the use of residential fire sprinkler systems is growing, and many water utilities need guidance to assist them in creating their own policies, procedures, and regulations regarding the use of these systems.

The design approaches for residential fire sprinkler systems include many unique aspects that differ from the traditional fire connections to commercial, industrial, and multi-unit residential buildings. For instance, while traditional fire-protection systems for commercial and industrial buildings are usually designed under the NFPA 13 or NFPA 13R Standard and frequently require a separate and distinct line for the fire supply, residential fire sprinkler systems under the NFPA 13D Standard provide several design options, including separate fire lines or a single, multi-purpose line that provides both the domestic water supply and fire supply from the water main. While this publication does not provide detailed design guidance on residential fire sprinkler systems, it identifies important implications of these systems to service line and meter sizing, and identifies appropriate references for readers to seek detailed guidance.

AWWA MANUALS RELATED TO METERING AND SERVICE LINES

AWWA publishes several manuals of water supply practices that are focused on water meters and service lines. Manual M22 is one of a suite of manuals that form AWWA's core metering and service line guidance documents. A brief summary of AWWA manuals related to metering is presented below.

- **M1,** *Principles of Water Rates, Fees, and Charges,* **sixth edition (2012)**—provides financial managers, water policymakers, and rate analysts with relevant information needed to evaluate and select water rate structures, fees, charges, and pricing policies.

- **M6,** *Water Meters: Selection, Installation, Testing, and Maintenance,* **fifth edition (2012)**—provides a complete manual of practice for water utilities on the selection, installation, operation, and maintenance of customer water meters and also provides sample record-keeping forms, a history of water-use measurement, and the development of modern water meters. M6 is heavily illustrated with photos, diagrams, and performance requirements.

- **M33,** *Flowmeters in Water Supply,* **second edition (2006)**—describes in detail the design and operation of commonly used flowmeters in water systems.

This page intentionally blank.

Chapter **2**

Consumer Water Demands, Trends, and Considerations

INTRODUCTION

Peak customer demand is an important factor in many elements of the design of a water utility's production and distribution capacity and in customer metering. The maximum day demands often are used for sizing of water treatment plants,[*] and peak instantaneous demands, along with fire flows, are critical for sizing treated water storage and distribution systems. Another important use of peak instantaneous demands, and the main topic of this manual, is for sizing service lines and meters for individual customers.

Updates to recent end-use studies and additional datasets obtained from a broad range of utilities provide useful information for evaluating tap, meter, and service line sizing. This topic can be controversial, because many utilities obtain revenue based on the size of the water meter or water tap and thus may have an incentive to require larger meters. Increasing the size of meters, however, is expensive to the customer and often leads to inaccurate meter registration, poor engineering, and a potential loss of revenue to the utility. In contrast, from the developer's perspective, there is an incentive to downsize meters and taps, which can cause poor service to the customer and higher maintenance

---

[*] Because of the high cost of providing treatment, some utilities have trended toward using peak flows over a longer period, of perhaps 2 to 5 days, and relying on system storage to meet peak demands above treatment capacity. Such an approach has serious water quality implications, however. The Water Industry Database (AWWA and AwwaRF 1992) indicates an average distribution system retention time of 1.3 days and a maximum retention time of 3.0 days based on a survey of more than 800 US utilities.

costs to the utility. Some utilities have solved this problem by setting tap fees based on the anticipated water demand of a customer, which then enable the meter to be right-sized without regard to utility revenue.

Properly sizing water meters and service lines is made more complicated by the lack of historical data on which to base estimates of peak instantaneous demands or flow ranges. This lack of comprehensive current information has caused a reliance on procedures developed in the 1970s that may not be appropriate for today's building designs. Fortunately, advances in electronics and metering have provided new tools that promise to greatly facilitate collection of demand data and hence, increase the ability to predict peak flow and flow range estimates. This third edition of M22 includes updates from a sampling of typical residential demand patterns in different utilities but does not include data systematically collected for the purpose of evaluating meter and line sizing for non-residential customers.

The peak instantaneous demand for any customer is a function of the number and type of water-using devices on the site and the probability that a given number of these will be operated simultaneously. One method to determine peak demands of existing customers is to collect empirical information as described in chapter 3. Another method is the use of fixture values and corresponding demand curves based on similar buildings. The fixture value method may be the only practical option when sizing meters and service lines for new customers. This edition of Manual M22 includes additional references to the latest edition of AWWA Manual M6, *Water Meters—Selection, Installation, Testing, and Maintenance,* which is provided for meter selection and capacity. The remainder of this chapter discusses demand patterns of municipal water customers and some new approaches for obtaining data on peak demands and ranges of flow, which can be used to improve demand estimates.

WATER-USE TRENDS

Background

A common method for determining per capita water use is to divide the sum of water used in a given period by the total number of people served. The type of customer base, climate, irrigated area, and efficiency of use thus influence per capita water use for a water utility. In the 20th century, urban per-capita use first increased as households installed new water-using devices and fixtures and then decreased as federal plumbing codes and national standards required these products to be more water efficient. Currently North America is in a period of declining per capita water use.

Up until 1980, urban per-capita water use in the US increased from an annual average of about 60 gal per capita per day (gpcd) in 1920 to about 180 gpcd in the 1970s. During a 30-year period from 1940 to 1970, per capita water use doubled, increasing from 85 gpcd to 175 gpcd. Since the late 1980s, indoor per-capita use has leveled or declined across the United States. A Water Research Foundation (WRF) study, *North America Residential Water Usage Trends Since 1992,* found that in 2008 a typical American household used 12,000 gal per year less than in 1978 (Coomes, P. et al. 2010).

Nationally, per capita indoor residential water use ranges between 30 gpcd and 70 gpcd, while outdoor residential use varies widely (DeOreo et al. 2012). Outdoor use is driven by climate, weather events, irrigated landscape area, the type of plant material, and the irrigation method. Differences in water demands between communities are due to several factors, including differences in climate and average lot size and differences in the age of the housing stock, where older homes use more water than newer homes equipped with modern efficient fixtures and appliances.

Water use in the nonresidential sector within a given climate zone tends to be more site-specific. This tendency is especially true in the industrial sector in which use is often dependent on employees and irrigated landscape demand. The WRF is presently conducting a study of nonresidential water use patterns.

Residential Per-Capita Use

Per capita water use in the residential sector has declined nationally since the 1990s. The national WRF 2014 *Residential End Uses of Water Update* study measured the average indoor daily per-capita water use from nine different cities to be approximately 52.6 gpcd normalized for a household of three (DeOreo et al. 2014) and is 15.4 percent lower normalized use measured using identical techniques in 1999 (Mayer et al., 1999).

Prior to 1980, no standards existed for water use volumes or flow rates for indoor household fixtures. In 1980, the maximum volume standard for toilets was established at 3.5 gal/flush. Table 2-1 shows the national fixture standards for US manufacturers that went into effect in January 1994 as part of the 1992 Energy Policy Act. The conversion to high-efficiency fixtures has had a major impact on annual average demand and daily peak instantaneous water demands, because they affect the peak flow for each device. Prior to the 1992 legislation, toilet flush volumes of 5 gal and showerhead flow rates of 5 to 10 gpm were common. Some of these high flow fixtures remain in use, but they are gradually being replaced.

Recently, national water efficiency programs such as USEPA-WaterSense and local green building codes, such as the California CalGREEN code, have encouraged and mandated water efficiency beyond the 1992 Energy Policy Act requirements. The national EnergySTAR program has resulted in more water efficient and more energy-efficient clothes washers and dishwashers being manufactured that have provided additional indoor efficiencies. High-efficiency clothes washers use about 35 percent of the water of the clothes washers of the 1990s. Approved changes to Department of Energy clothes washer standards will ensure that only water- and energy-efficient machines will be available for purchase in the future. Recent residential water use research has documented statistically significant reductions in indoor per-capita water use with the majority of the water savings coming from increased efficiency in toilets, clothes washers, and faucets (DeOreo and Mayer 2012).

Outdoor water use is driven by the size of the irrigated landscape, type of plant material, and weather. The flow rate for automated irrigation systems can be controlled, however, by the design criteria and, thus, impact meter and service-line sizing to some degree. For existing sites, automated irrigation systems can often be designed based on the size of the existing water meter and service line. In these cases, flow rates are determined by the number and flow rates of the sprinkler heads (or emitters) for each station

Table 2-1   National fixture standards

Fixture	1992 Standards	Previous Standards
Showerheads	2.5 gpm	3.0 gpm
Lavatory and kitchen faucets	2.2 gpm	3.0 gpm
Metering faucets	0.25 gpm	—
Gravity, flushometer tank, and electro-mechanical hydraulic-type toilets	1.6 gal/flush	3.5 gal/flush
Blowout toilets	3.5 gal/flush (found in airports, stadiums, etc.) NOTE: Some states prohibit blow-out at 3.5 gpf	—
Urinals	1.0 gal/flush	3.5 gal/flush

(also called *valves* or *zones*). Besides landscape irrigation, other outdoor consumptive uses include water for pools, spas, ponds, and vehicle and hardscape cleaning. Although the percent break-down of these outdoor uses would vary widely around the country and from customer to customer, the largest percent of use on average is for landscape irrigation. In the Southwest, outdoor residential use can account for over 50 percent of the total residential annual use. More utilities are offering irrigation-specific water meters for residential use, meaning utilities will install two separate meters at homes with irrigation systems. These meters help identify the single largest residential water use and allow utilities enhanced control over water irrigation during droughts. These meters tend to improve conservation when homeowners can identify where water is used.

Per capita indoor water use has declined significantly over the past 15 years, and the efficiency standards already in place coupled with building codes that are increasingly focused on water and energy efficiency will result in further demand reductions. Outdoor water use has also decreased in some regions; however, outdoor use is more variable and subject to the impacts of the prevailing climate. As average temperatures increase, the water requirement of landscapes will also increase, which could result in increased irrigation demands. Such changes are difficult to predict, and regional differences in water supply and climate are likely to have a significant impact on water use. Toilets now available in the United States use dual-flush technology to reduce water use to only 0.8 gal/flush on one setting and 1.6 gal/flush on another setting. As a general rule, in the United States, most single-family residential demands occur below 8 gpm, with the peaking demand typically below 25 gpm. Higher peak single-family residential demands may occur in properties located in arid climates or with larger lot sizes (i.e., greater than 10,000 ft^2).

Nonresidential Use—Improved Efficiency

In the nonresidential sector, commonly called commercial, industrial, and institutional, or CII, water demand trends are more difficult to predict because of the wide variety of land uses, manufacturing processes, and inherent site-specific differences. As demand stresses existing water supply sources, as the cost of water increases, and as incentives are provided to reduce demand, there will be increased efforts to ensure that water is used as efficiently as possible. The general trend, therefore, is toward increased efficiencies of use and perhaps lower peak demands versus historical norms.

Some recent trends to improve nonresidential water use efficiency include: (1) increasing cooling system efficiencies; (2) switching from water-cooled to air-cooled ice machines and refrigerant compressors; (3) increasing water use efficiency in restrooms; (4) improving the efficiencies of water using processes and eliminating single-pass cooling; (5) increasing water use efficiency in commercial kitchens; (6) water reuse or recycling in car washes, commercial dishwashers, and other industrial and commercial water-using processes; and (7) utility incentive programs.

WATER USE PATTERNS

Residential Use

A 1999 study of residential water use patterns (Mayer et al. 1999) sponsored by the WRF found:
1.   Two daily peaks of use: one occurring between 7:00 a.m. and 9:00 a.m., and the other occurring between 6:00 p.m. and 8:00 p.m.
2.   96.5 percent of the peak daily indoor instantaneous flow rates were below 10 gpm, and 52.0 percent were below 6 gpm.

3. The average daily indoor consumption was 69.3 gpcd, and the median daily indoor consumption was 60.1 gpcd. Indoor water use did not vary significantly between winter and summer seasons.

4. Outdoor water use is highly variable and depends largely on the local climate and precipitation, the type of landscape installed, and the irrigation method (manual versus automatic).

Typical single-family indoor use with no conservation is shown in Table 2.2. The following data was gathered during 1996–99 (without conservation) and during 2009–10 (with conservation). The "without conservation" water use is typical of homes built in the 1970s and 1980s with 3.5 gpf toilets and top-loading clothes washers. The "with conservation" water use is typical of new homes built to the 2012 WaterSense New Home Specification, which includes 1.28 gpf toilets and high-efficiency clothes washers designed to use less than 15 gal per load.

Nonresidential Use

Although it was previously stated that nonresidential use tends to be site-specific, ranges of use can be found for different business classes, such as schools, hospitals, offices, restaurants, etc. Per-account use is shown in Table 2-3 for 23 selected business classes in the East Bay Municipal Utility District service area in the San Francisco Bay Area. This table is presented primarily for illustrative purposes. Average use in each category may vary considerably from community to community and from customer to customer.

Evaluating nonresidential uses requires a comprehensive water assessment of all known water uses in the facility. Understanding how water will be used within a facility is the foundation for proper meter and line sizing. Each facility type has different water use patterns, depending on its function and use. While the equipment and processes vary widely, there are opportunities in all commercial and institutional buildings to achieve significant water savings indoors and outdoors by making improvements in operational areas.

Submetering by the facility to routinely monitor component water use allows building owners and operators to more effectively understand and manage facility water use. Submetering allows a facility to quickly find and fix leaks or other unnecessary water use. The added benefit is that the facility is able to identify cost-effective water use reduction opportunities and to track project savings.

Table 2-2   Per-capita residential indoor use

Inside Water Use	Without Conservation		With Conservation	
	percent	*gpcd*	*percent*	*gpcd*
Toilet	27	18.5	15	6.0
Shower	17	11.6	33	12.8
Bath	2	1.2	3	1.2
Laundry	22	15.0	11	4.4
Dishwashing	1	1.0	2	0.6
Faucets	16	10.9	17	6.7
Leaks	4	9.5	19	7.3
Total	**89**	**67.7**	**100**	**39.0**

Source: DeOreo and Mayer (2012).

Table 2-3   Average per-account consumption and monthly peaking factors* for selected customer types in San Francisco Bay area†

Business Type	Annual Average Consumption, gpd	Monthly Peaking Factor	Business Type	Annual Average Consumption, gpd	Monthly Peaking Factor
Bakeries	3,500	1.2	Offices	1,100	1.7
Bakeries (bread)	6,000	1.0	Hotels (with food)	7,000	1.3
Printers	1,000	1.1	Hotels (without food)	4,000	1.2
Retail	500	1.3	Commercial laundries	4,000	1.0
Groceries	800	1.5	Laundromats	4,000	1.0
Gas stations	500	1.6	Industrial laundries	50,000	1.1
Fast-food restaurants	1,000	1.4	Car washes	3,000	2.0
Restaurants	1,500	1.1	Auto repair	300	1.3
Night clubs	900	1.1	Parks	7,000	12.0
Cemeteries	7,000	9.0	Hospitals	15,000	1.3
Large apartments	3,000	1.3	Schools	6,000	2.0
Apartments (2-4 units)	500	1.2			

* Summer (July and August) use over winter (December and January) use.

† East Bay Municipal Utility District consumption data.

REFERENCES

Bowen, P.T., J.F. Harp, J.W. Baxter, and R.D. Shull. 1993. *Residential Water Use Patterns.* Denver, Colo.: American Water Works Association and American Water Works Association Research Foundation (AwwaRF).

California Department of Water Resources. 1998. *California Water Plan Update.* Bulletin 160-98, pp. 4–17.

Coomes, P.T., J.R. Rockaway, and B. Kornstein. 2010. *North America Residential Water Usage Trends Since 1992.* Water Research Foundation (WRF) and U.S. Environmental Protection Agency (USEPA).

DeOreo, W.B. and P.W. Mayer. 2012. *Insights Into Declining Single-Family Water Demands.* Jour. AWWA, 104(6).

DeOreo, B., P. Mayer, J. Kiefer, and B. Dziegielewski. 2012. *Residential End-Uses of Water: Progress Report and Interim Results.* WRF. *Drinking Water Research.* 22-3 (7–9).

Mayer, P.W., W.B. DeOreo, E. Opitz, J. Kiefer, B. Dziegielewski, and J.O. Nelson. 1999. *Residential End Uses of Water.* Denver, Colo.: AwwaRF.

USEPA. 2006. *Growing Toward More Efficient Water Use: Linking Development, Infrastructure, and Drinking Water Policies.* Accessed online January 2006: http://www.epa.gov/smartgrowth/pdf/growing_water_use_efficiency.pdf.

USEPA. 2012. *WaterSense at Work: Best Management Practices for Commercial and Institutional Facilities.* Washington D.C.: USEPA.

Chapter **3**

Meter Sizing Using Customer Usage Data

ACCURATELY MEASURING CUSTOMER USAGE

Customer usage data is typically generated by attaching an electronic flow recorder directly to a customer's water meter and logging the actual customer usage over very short increments of time. In so doing, a customer-specific demand profile is created, which accurately represents that customer's water-use characteristics.

Demand profiles generated from existing accurate water meters are uniquely valuable, because a water meter represents the most precise means to measure potable water use. Flow recorders, like the one shown in Figure 3-1, accomplish their mission without interrupting the accurate registration of the water meter and, typically, without altering the existing meter configuration. In a small number of cases, adapters are required and easily installed.

Applications for customer demand profiles may be grouped into three general categories: (1) meter sizing and maintenance, (2) water use audits, and (3) cost-of-service studies. While only the first category is discussed in detail in this manual, the same data gathered for meter-sizing purposes has other important uses and can benefit a variety of utility functions, including distribution, metering, conservation, customer service, engineering, planning, and finance. In the case of water use audits, demand profiles assist with conservation programs, leak detection, customer service, and hydraulic modeling. For cost-of-service studies, demand profiles are used to obtain data regarding the variability of use by residential, commercial, industrial, and wholesale customer-class groups. Because the same data can support these applications, when collecting the data, all of the potential applications must be considered for which the data may be of value presently or in the future. For example, if a cost-of-service study

Figure 3-1 Flow recorder and water meter
Courtesy of F.S. Brainard and Co.

or hydraulic model requires only hourly demand data, one may still choose to store the data in 10-, 30-, or 60-sec increments so that the same data can be used effectively for meter sizing and maintenance programs. An example of a software program that uses demand profile data to determine appropriate meter sizing is provided in appendix A.

Flow recorders have been used to size meters since the 1930s, and although the technology has changed a great deal since then, recorders remain the most accurate meter-sizing methodology when an accurate meter exists from which to record. Alternative methods to gauge water use, such as pipe size or fixture count, do not provide the actual usage patterns that are essential for determining the ideal meter type and size.

In general, a demand profile should accurately provide peak-usage rate data and the percentage and volume of water used in critical flow rate ranges. Critical flow ranges would include, as a minimum, flow rates below the specified accuracy range of a meter, flow rates at the cross-over range in a compound meter setting, flow rates greater than the midpoint of a meter's specified flow range, and maximum flow rates. The objective is to minimize the size of the meter (and its cost) for maximum accuracy and revenue recovery without adversely affecting meter reliability, pressure levels, or fire-flow requirements. Meter maintenance costs are important to consider. It may be that a 6-in. turbine meter could better serve a customer with constant flows of 600 gpm than a 4-in. turbine; while both would accurately measure the flows, the 6-in. turbine would experience less degradation from wear and tear. The more closely a meter is matched to a customer's usage pattern, the more water will be accurately measured and billed.

Tim Edgar, in *The Large Water Meter Handbook*, first edition, illustrates this potential revenue gain with the case of a 100-unit apartment building with a 4-in. turbine meter. The actual monthly consumption was 500,000 gal, but much of that volume was at low-flow rates. Because the turbine meter was less accurate at flow rates below 12 gpm, 15 percent of the volume went unrecorded and unbilled in both water and, as is very often the case, sewer charges. The result was a revenue loss of $1,700.00 per year (at $3/1,000 gal for combined water and sewer). As Edgar points out, if a utility has 100 such incorrectly sized meters, those 100 meters would cost a utility over one million dollars in lost revenue over six years.

As another example, the Boston Water and Sewer Commission began a downsizing program in the early 1990s. John Sullivan, Boston's director of engineering at the time, reported in presentations to the American Water Works Association that, between August

1990 and April 1992, the city had accounted for an additional 113,784 ft^3 of water per day (0.8 mgd). With just the meters downsized in the first year of the program, Boston anticipated the total increase in revenue over five years for combined water and sewer to be $6.8 million (1991 dollars). Such savings would only be realized in systems with many oversized turbine meters, which underestimate throughput at low-flow rates.

While the most direct benefit of proper meter sizing is increased revenue and accountability, meters offer a distribution system much more value than just revenue enhancement. Any decision made by a utility related to water usage can only be as good as the consumption data collected from meters. In general, demand profiles provide valuable data to improve distribution system design, performance, and management. In addition to increasing supply/customer demand, water balance accuracy, and revenue, demand profiles help to identify service size requirements, clarify meter maintenance requirements, define and improve water use characteristics, enhance customer satisfaction and awareness, and establish equitable and justifiable rate structures.

With increased water scarcity, conservation has also become an important industry issue. For many utilities, conservation has become the most cost-effective means to increase water resource availability. All of these distribution system design, performance, and management objectives are dependent on the capability of a system's meters to account for usage as accurately as possible, which can only occur as a consequence of sizing and typing meters properly.

RECORDER DESIGN

Theory of Operation

Demand profiles are generated with electronic flow recorders. The portable flow recorders discussed herein are also referred to as *demand profilers*, *demand recorders*, and *loggers*. These devices collect data from a meter's internal drive magnets, a meter's pointer movement, or the meter's integral digital or analog output and then stores the data for later downloading and analysis. Recorders can be moved from one meter site to the next with minimum effort, and they work with standard meters, thereby eliminating the need for special registers. If a magnetic or optical sensor is used, it is typically either strapped to the outside of a meter using Velcro, cable ties, or heavy-duty tape, or is integral to an adapter located between the meter body and the existing register.

Because of adverse operating conditions (meter pits, temperature extremes, rough handling, public access), recorders should be submersible, durable, and securable. In order to provide extended data storage capability in remote locations, recorders should also offer substantial battery life.

Recording Methods

Data formats can be divided into three categories: pulse (or count), encoder, and analog (e.g., 4–20 mA or variable voltage). Flow recorders typically use pulse data and sometimes encoder data. Analog formats are rarely used in demand profiling. Although the analog formats are not explicitly discussed in this chapter, the following information should assist if an analog output is the only option available.

A frequently used solution for getting pulse data from existing meter installations that do not have a built-in pulse output is a magnetic flux sensor. Flow recorders using magnetic pick-ups sense the magnetic field generated by the magnetic coupling of a water meter's internal drive magnets and convert the magnetic flux change into a digital pulse that is logged into memory and later downloaded for analysis. Optical pick-up recorders sense the meter pointer passing beneath the sensor and also store the signal as digital pulses to be downloaded later. Some solutions, including AMI (advanced metering infrastructure)/ AMR (automatic meter reading), use an encoder interface, in which case a prior meter reading is subtracted from the current reading to calculate the volume of water for each interval. Some newer meters incorporate pulse output options that can be used for gathering usage data. In the case of pulse data, each pulse is associated with a known volume of water.

The principal advantage of a magnetic pick-up is the higher resolution of data made possible by the rotation speed of a meter's internal drive magnets. In most cases, the drive magnets inside a meter rotate much faster than the sweep hand (pointer) on the register's dial face. In small meters, the number of magnet rotations per unit of time can be as high as approximately 30 per sec at 20 gpm. At this rate, the magnets are rotating 900 times as fast as the sweep hand. In the case of turbine meters, the rotation speed of the magnets can vary greatly, from approximately 800 times the speed of the sweep hand to the same speed as the sweep hand. An advantage of using a meter's pulse or encoder output is the avoidance of any risk of electromagnetic interference from other equipment in proximity to a meter that a magnetic flux sensor can potentially detect. Some new meters no longer use magnets to couple the meter register with its base, which eliminates magnetic sensors as a signal-sensing option in such cases. Optical and mechanical adapters enable compatibility with older gear-driven meters that preceded magnetic-drive meters.

Magnetic Sensors

Because most meters have the magnetic coupling directly under the register, a reliable signal can be detected by placing the sensor on the side of the register as shown in Figure 3-2. Without exception, if present, the magnetic coupling is directly under the register in the case of all 2-in. and smaller positive displacement and multi-jet meters. With larger meters, if the magnetic coupling is not directly under the register, it is typically in the center of the turbine rotor in the middle of the flow. In this case, the magnetic sensor must be placed on the side of the meter body in order to be as close to the drive magnets as possible.

If the magnetic coupling is under the register, but the register has shielding on the sides, the sensor may have to be located directly on top of the register in order to circumvent the shield. Because the recorder's magnetic sensor is essentially picking up the electromagnetic noise generated by a water meter, the sensor can be susceptible to picking up noise generated by other sources of electromagnetic noise, such as motors, generators, and alarm systems. The recorder's sensing circuitry should be designed to consistently pick up the magnetic signal generated by a water meter's drive magnets, while minimizing the potential for picking up electromagnetic noise from other sources.

Data Storage Capacity

It is essential that a recorder have adequate data storage capacity to enable the recorder to store a substantial amount of data. As discussed in greater detail in the "Data storage interval" section, flow data must be logged into memory in small time increments if accurate maximum and minimum flow rate data is to be ensured. The potential factor of difference in the observed maximum flow rate between a 10-sec and a 60-sec data storage interval monitoring the exact same flow is 6:1. The potential factor of difference in the observed maximum flow rate between a 10-sec and a 300-sec (5 min) data storage interval monitoring the exact same flow is 30:1. In other words, if a solitary flow usage of 200 gal occurred for just 10 sec at a rate of 1,200 gpm, whereas the 10-sec data storage interval could detect this high flow rate of 1,200 gpm, the 300-sec data storage interval would observe a maximum flow rate of just 40 gpm because the 200 gal would get averaged over 5 min rather than averaged over 10 sec.

Figure 3-2   Flow recorder stores a demand profile from a 3-in. water meter

Courtesy of F.S. Brainard and Co.

Obviously, this difference could have serious implications for a meter size selection. Frequently, users choose to collect and store premise water-use data for one week when assessing the size of a commercial user's meter in order to ensure that a representative sample of flow data is gathered. If a user is to store 10-sec interval data for one week, the recorder must be able to continuously store a minimum of 60,480 intervals of data. For other applications, such as cost-of-service studies and hydraulic modeling, a smaller data storage capacity is required than for meter sizing. If the same data is to be used most efficiently, however, the storage capacity should provide for high resolution data so that the same data may be used effectively for the various other applications.

Data Storage Interval

This interval is the period of time over which a flow recorder counts pulses before that interval's pulse count is logged into memory. The interval determines the resolution of the raw data file from which all subsequent graphs and reports are generated: the shorter the interval, the greater the detail possible in subsequent graphs and reports. For example, a data storage interval of 10 sec allows accurate data analysis for periods of 10 sec or longer. As long as the graph/report generating software allows for adjustment of the time interval over which flow rates and volumes are calculated, the data storage interval should be kept short, e.g., 10 sec.

Keeping the data storage interval small is essential for accurately determining maximum flow rates. To ensure the accurate identification of a maximum flow rate, the data storage interval cannot exceed 50 percent of the duration of a maximum flow event. For example, if an industrial customer has a particular operation that occurs just once each 30 min, lasts 30 sec, and uses 500 gal of water (i.e., a demand of 1,000 gpm for 30 sec), identification of the 1,000-gpm flow rate can only be assured if data is logged into memory at least once each 15 sec. If the data storage interval is between 15 sec and 30 sec, there is an increasing likelihood that the maximum flow rate will be understated, because no data storage interval is guaranteed to begin and end within the 30-sec event. If the data storage interval is more than 30 sec, the true maximum flow rate will not be detected; the maximum flow rate will be understated. In this particular example, a data storage interval of 15 sec or less would show the 1,000-gpm flow rate.

However, if the data storage interval is 15 min (900 sec), the maximum flow rate would appear as only 33 gpm because all that is known is that a total of 500 gal was used during a 15 min period. If the data storage interval is 5 min, a maximum flow rate of 100 gpm would be indicated. As can be seen, a serious meter sizing error can easily be made if the recorded data is not collected and stored at a time interval resolution sufficient to capture the actual maximum flow rate.

As another example, if a utility customer has an operation that periodically uses 250 gal of water for 10 sec (which equates to a rate of 1,500 gpm) in addition to its other uses, this scenario is graphically simulated in the following three graphs (see Figures 3-3, 3-4, and 3-5). In each case, the exact same data was used to create each graph. The only difference is the time interval selected for maximum and minimum flow rate calculations. In the first case, flow rates are analyzed using a 10-sec interval. In the second case, an interval of 60 sec is used for rate calculations. In the third case, an interval of 300 sec is used.

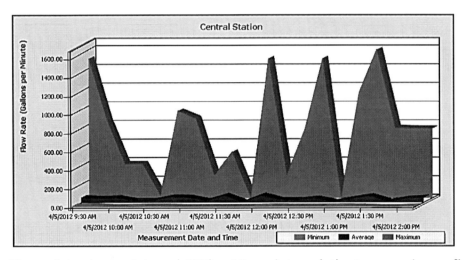

Figure 3-3   10-sec data storage interval. With a 10-sec interval, the true maximum flow rate of 1,500 gpm is identified.

Courtesy of F.S. Brainard and Co.

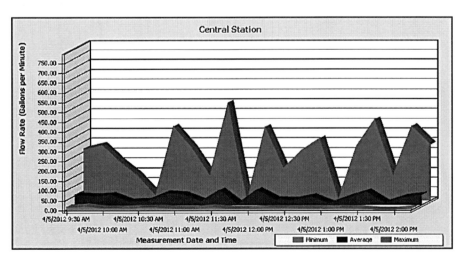

Figure 3-4   60-sec data storage interval. With a 60-sec interval, the maximum flow rate is reduced to about 500 gpm.

Courtesy of F.S. Brainard and Co.

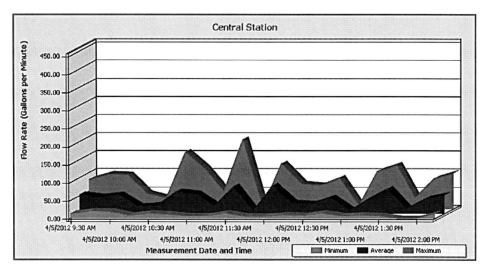

Figure 3-5   300-sec data storage interval. With a 300-sec (5-min) interval, the maximum flow rate is further reduced to less than 200 gpm.

Courtesy of F.S. Brainard and Co.

There are disadvantages to making the data storage interval too small. This interval defines the size of the downloaded data file and the length of time that one can record before running out of recorder memory. The same test recorded with a 5-sec interval will take up six times more memory than one stored with a 30 sec interval. Generally, a 10-sec interval provides adequate detail and recording time for most applications. If one is making a long recording (multiple weeks) and a 10-sec interval would use up all of the logger's memory before the recording is completed, lengthen the data storage interval. Another problem with too short an interval is discussed in the following section, "Meter Pulse Resolution." Briefly, if too short an interval is used on a meter with slow-moving drive magnets (or sweep hand, in the case of optical sensors), skewing (exaggeration) of maximum and minimum flow rates can occur, because there is too little data for accurate calculations. A recorder's operating instructions should identify such meters so that care is taken when selecting intervals for data presentation. Software design can also provide some correction when downloading raw data from a recorder.

Meter Pulse Resolution

This resolution is defined as the number of pulses generated by a meter that equate to a unit of liquid measure. For magnetic pick-ups, the resolution is the number of meter magnet poles (as the internal drive magnets rotate) that equate to a unit of liquid measure. It is desirable that the internal magnets revolve as fast as possible without degrading the reliability of the meter; accordingly, the higher the number of magnet poles per unit of measure, the better. Faster magnets generate more pulses, which translate to greater data accuracy. For optical pick-ups, the same considerations apply to the speed of sweep hand rotation.

The pulse resolution (or factor) is especially important when determining maximum and minimum flow rates. The issues are very similar to those discussed in the preceding section, "Data Storage Interval." Concerning maximum flow rates, if a magnet (or sweep hand) is rotating slowly, a large, short-term usage could take place without any evidence of its occurrence. For example, if a 6-in. turbine meter generates just one magnetic pulse for each 500 gal, while another 6-in. turbine generates one pulse for each 2 gal, the 250-gal usage at 1,500 gpm described in the preceding section might not even be identified at all by a recorder attached to the 6-in. turbine with the slow-moving magnets, while the 6-in. turbine with the fast moving magnets would have provided 125 pulses to the recorder. Furthermore, if the recorder attached to the meter with the slow moving magnets did detect one pulse within a 10-sec interval, the recorder technology might erroneously assume that 500 gal were used during that 10-sec interval, which would equate to a flow rate of 3,000 gpm. It equates to a flow rate of 3,000 gpm because, if one pulse is logged in 10 sec, this is the equivalent of six pulses per min, and six pulses per min multiplied by 500 gal per pulse equals 3,000 gpm. Accordingly, a meter with fast moving magnets can provide continuously accurate data throughout the flow ranges, whereas a meter with slow moving magnets cannot. Likewise, using optical sensors, the faster the rotation of the sweep hand, the more accurate the resultant data. As previously noted, intelligent software design can recognize and account for such circumstances.

Minimum flow rates identify leakage rates and impact the selection of turbine versus compound meters in larger flow rate applications. To ensure the accurate identification of minimum flow rates, as with maximum flow rates, a user must know which meters have slow moving drive magnets. For example, if a meter's magnets are providing just one pulse for each 20 gal, and the current flow rate is a steady rate of just 5 gpm, only one pulse will be generated each 4 min. If one observes the data in time increments smaller than once each 4 min, the flow rate will appear to vary between zero and some amount greater than the actual flow rate of 5 gpm. As an illustration, if a 1-min data storage interval is used, the flow rate will appear to equal zero for 3 of each 4 min, and 20 gpm for 1 of each 4 min, because each pulse, equaling 20 gal apiece, will appear just once each 4 min when a steady flow rate of 5 gpm is occurring. If a 4-min time interval is used to observe the data, it will appear as if a steady flow rate of 5 gpm is occurring.

The two graphs shown in Figures 3-6A and 3-6B represent the scenario just described. Both graphs were generated from the exact same data, but the time increments used to view the data are 1 and 4 min, respectively. Each pulse from the meter equals 20 gal, and they were spaced 4 min apart (except during the initial interval shown). Software design can help by evaluating the data to determine the likelihood that raw pulse data should be averaged over longer periods of time.

Unless someone is actually at the meter site watching the meter at the time of the event, it is not possible to know with certainty whether a periodic use of 20 gal is occurring or a steady flow rate of 5 gpm is occurring. If each pulse from the meter equaled a smaller amount of water, such as one gallon, the recorder technology would be able to consistently display more accurate data.

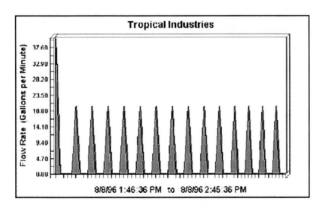

A: Storage interval of 4 min

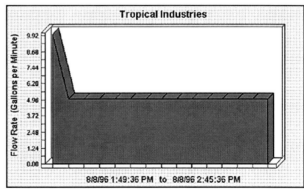

B: Storage interval of 1 min

Figure 3-6   Figure A and B—4-min and 1-min data storage intervals

Courtesy of F.S. Brainard and Co.

The key to getting accurate flow data is generating a sufficient number of pulses per time interval, while keeping the storage interval as small as possible. In the case of magnetic pulses, all 2-in. and smaller positive displacement and multi-jet meters provide a good pulse resolution, such that the data can reasonably be observed in time increments as small as 10 sec. Because some turbine meters have magnets that rotate relatively slowly, low flow rates are difficult to accurately observe.

Accordingly, adapters that increase the magnetic pulse resolution can be useful in determining accurate flow rate data because the flow data may be accurately logged and viewed in smaller time increments. One compound adapter, for example, can increase the resolution by a factor of 12 on various compound- and turbine-type meters (Figures 3-7 and 3-8). The adapter installs easily and enables the existing register to continue functioning normally. The same considerations also apply when using optical sensors.

Figure 3-7   Compound adapter and sensor

Courtesy of F.S. Brainard and Co.

Figure 3-8   Recording demand profiles from large compound meters may require an adapter

Courtesy of F.S. Brainard and Co.

RECORDING DATA

Length of Record

As previously discussed, many recorder users choose to store data from commercial sites for one week because certain high-rate water uses, e.g., a manufacturing operation, may only occur on a particular day each week. If possible, water usage should be discussed with a customer prior to storing data to ensure that the duration of the recording period is sufficient to get a representative sample of the full range of flow data. In the case of multi-tenant residential or hotels/motels, 24 hr of data may be sufficient as long as the data is collected during hot weather for residential and high occupancy for hotels/motels. Understanding a user's water use characteristics is important in order to select the optimum length of the data storage period. Experience with different types of users over time will also provide an indication as to the optimum record length for different classes of users.

Customer Water Use Patterns

Data should be recorded during a period in which the user experiences typical peak, average, and minimum flow rates, and for a duration sufficient to capture those rates. For example, data should not be recorded at a school or factory during a vacation period. Similarly, as previously mentioned, utility personnel may want to record data for at least a week at an industrial site if there is evidence that the customer performs different operations on different days of the week. Seasonal cycles are as important to consider as weekly ones. Weather at different times of the year may substantially alter demand patterns, especially if outdoor irrigation use is recorded through the same meter. If a customer uses a lot more water on a hot summer day, data on such a day should be recorded to capture peak flow data for meter typing, sizing, and accuracy evaluations.

Potential changes in demand patterns should be anticipated. At a residential development, the number of additional units currently under construction should be considered. Also, a user should be resurveyed if the type of use changes. Commercial lease space can have a high rate of turnover. A bottling company could be replaced by a warehousing or distribution company with substantially lower water usage. If the meter is not resized, the new user could be the beneficiary of a lot of free water inaccurately measured at low flow rates.

Meter Accuracy

When a flow recorder is used, the assumption is that the meter being monitored is accurate. A flow recorder cannot determine meter accuracy, but it can determine the accurate meter type and size for an existing meter site. Because a flow recorder is only as accurate as the meter to which it is attached, routine meter testing is important when using recorders to determine the appropriate meter size. Because most meter inaccuracy involves underregistration of usage, a flow record on an underregistering meter can result in the selection of an undersized meter.

Ideally, a meter should be tested for accuracy and repaired/recalibrated if testing indicates that it is not accurate prior to recording data for meter sizing purposes. As discussed in the section "Meter Maintenance Considerations," a demand profile performed in conjunction with a flow test may indicate that all of the flow is occurring in an accurate range of the meter, even though the meter is not accurate throughout the flow ranges. If this is the case, the meter does not need to be repaired/recalibrated because no revenue is currently being lost.

Flow recorders should be considered a valuable companion tool as part of a meter test program. As referred to in the previous paragraph, a flow recorder can identify the percentage of flow in low-, medium-, and high-flow ranges. With this information, testing can be focused on the ranges in which most of the usage is occurring, and unnecessary and costly repairs can be avoided. If a flow record indicates that all of the flow at an oil refinery or brewery is occurring in a high-flow range, whether or not the meter is accurate at low and medium flow rates is not relevant.

Verifying Data Accuracy

A principal advantage of recording flow data directly from water meters rather than using alternative technologies, such as ultrasonic devices, is that the resultant flow data is based on and may be verified against the meter's registration. Graphs and reports generated from the data may be used with confidence, because a water meter is the most accurate and reliable means to measure potable water use. If the accuracy of the data generated with a flow recorder is not verified by comparing the total volume observed by the flow recorder to the total volume registered by the water meter itself during the data storage period, however, this key advantage is lost.

Verification of data accuracy is critical and is accomplished by (a) requiring the user to enter the beginning and ending meter readings when downloading data, and (b) having an accurate meter magnetic-pulse factor database so that the total volume registered by the meter may be compared to the total volume registered by the flow recorder. This procedure also requires the operator to take special care when making a record of the meter readings so that the numbers are accurate and include digits down to the decimal. In order to read a meter down to the decimal, a digit for all rotating dials and painted-on zeros must be read.

The sample software screen shown in Figure 3-9 requires the user to compare the meter's register volume to the flow recorder's observed volume. The numbers should either be extremely close or differ by an explicable margin. The software calculates register volume by subtracting the meter's beginning register reading from the ending register reading. This example is based on a magnetic pick-up. It calculates the recorder volume by multiplying the total magnetic pulse count for the entire recording period times the magnetic pulse factor for that meter in the software's database. An explicable difference between the two total volumes would include differences due to change gears used in some meters for calibration purposes. Because the change gears are used to speed up and slow down the register to match the activity in the meter's chamber, the recorder's volume could differ from the register's volume by as much as 15 percent, even though both the meter and the recorder may have functioned 100 percent accurately. The software screen shown in Figure 3-9 includes an automatic data conversion factor option so that the recorder's volume can automatically be calibrated to match the meter's volume 100 percent in such cases.

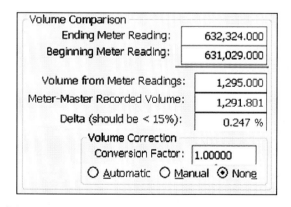

Figure 3-9   Verification of data accuracy

Courtesy of F.S. Brainard and Co.

Presentation Options

Software can present data in many formats and styles, as shown in Figure 3-10.

Generally, the flow recorder software should provide options to view volume data, max/avg/min flow rate data, and rate versus volume data. The two sample graphs shown in Figure 3-10 display rate versus volume data and max/avg/min flow rate data. The max/avg/min graph is useful for identifying instantaneous maximum and minimum flow rates and the timing and duration of events. The flow rate versus volume graph is useful for meter sizing and maintenance programs because it shows the percentage and volume of water used in various flow ranges.

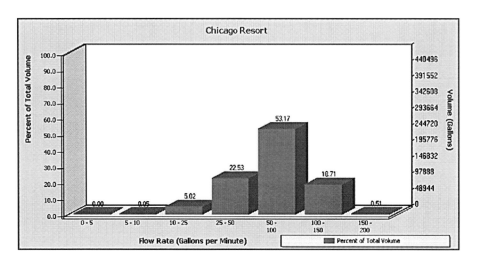

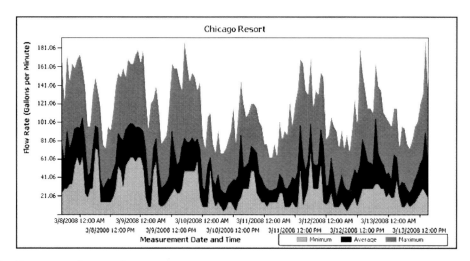

Figure 3-10   Presentation options

Courtesy of F.S. Brainard and Co.

USING CUSTOMER USAGE DATA

Summary of Meter Sizing Benefits

The use of demand profiles for meter sizing applies to all users except single-family residential. Standard meter size and water-use patterns characterize single-family residential customers. With users other than single-family residential, each customer generates a unique demand profile, and the meter should be sized accordingly. Although generic demand data can be developed for various customer class groups based on demographic and business information, the cost of gathering customer-specific demand data is minimal when compared to the revenue and community relations benefits associated with maximizing meter accuracy and water use accountability. An example of a software program that uses demand profile data to determine appropriate meter sizing is provided in appendix A.

Multi-family residential meters (e.g., apartment buildings) are the most consistently oversized meters due to both traditional fixture count methods of sizing and the advent of efficient, low use-rate fixtures. The graph displayed in Figure 3-11 is from an 8-in. wholesale connection serving a residential community. Although the specified accuracy range for an 8-in. turbine meter is approximately 40 gpm to 3,500 gpm, the flow rate never exceeded 40 gpm at this site. Accordingly, the customer received a lot of free water. Replacement of the meter with one that is properly sized will result in both greater meter accuracy and higher and more accurate utility revenue. The revenue gain is increased by higher sewer revenues whenever the sewer charge is a function of water usage.

Before downsizing a meter at an apartment complex or any other potentially large variable-use facility, the utility should make certain that there are no fire suppression systems served by that meter. If a fire suppression system is served by the meter, the meter may not be a good candidate for downsizing due to fire flow requirements. Moreover, either a UL-listed or FM-approved meter should be installed in this setting, preferably a fire service or comparable type of meter that is designed to accurately register usage across a wide range of flows, especially at flow rates below 7 gpm.

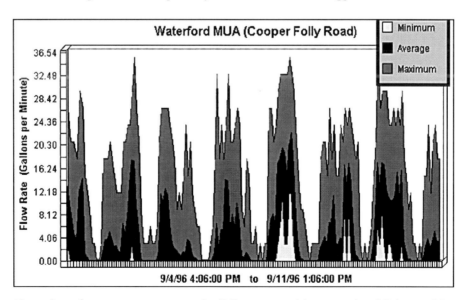

Figure 3-11   Flow data from an apartment building served by oversized 8-in. turbine meter

Courtesy of F.S. Brainard and Co.

Accurate meter sizing has positive residual effects with other programs mentioned in this manual. For example, a cost-of-service study in support of a rate structure design can only be fair and equitable if all of the sample sites have properly sized meters generating accurate usage data. Modern nonrevenue water management methods rely on accurate meter sizing. Customer-side leak detection efforts are undermined if a meter is oversized, because low flows are not detected, and the meter's pulse resolution is less than it would be with a smaller meter. Similarly, hydraulic models, conservation efforts, and other programs all benefit from accurate use registration, which is dependent on correct meter sizing.

Compound Versus Turbine Decisions

Utilities have differing philosophies concerning the application of compound versus turbine meters. Compound meters are more expensive and have higher maintenance costs, but they register accurately through a broader range of flows. Compound meters are typically appropriate for premises where people live (multi-family), work, and play, or where water use is expected 24 hr a day. By comparison, turbine meters are less expensive to purchase and maintain but offer a smaller accuracy range. For each meter application, there is an optimum solution, and a demand profile enables an operator to make the correct decision in each instance. If a compound meter is installed where a turbine is more appropriate, excessive maintenance costs and problems can be expected, and the utility will unnecessarily lose money. Conversely, if a turbine is installed where a compound is more appropriate, registration will be lost, and once again, the utility will unnecessarily lose money.

A rate versus volume graph enables an operator to determine the amount of flow occurring in the cross-over range of a compound meter. Within a compound meter's cross-over range, there is a substantial drop in accurate use registration because the turbine side of the compound setting is just starting to move, and, consequently, all flow through the turbine is below its accuracy range. If there is a meaningful amount of flow in the cross-over range, an alternative compound meter size or a single meter setting should be considered. A utility may consider installing one of the newer technology meters, such as floating ball turbine, ultrasonic, and electromagnetic (mag) meters, because they are similar to compound meters in that they can accurately measure usage at very low flow rates but do not have a cross-over valve that adversely affects both meter accuracy and maintenance costs.

Meter Maintenance Considerations

Another related use of customer usage data is meter maintenance programs, especially large meter maintenance programs. Some utilities consider demand profiles when making meter test, repair, and/or replacement decisions, because the demand data enables the utility to perform an accurate cost–benefit analysis of these three maintenance options on a case-by-case basis. For example, if a 10-in. turbine meter tests 100 percent accurate in a high-flow range, 90 percent accurate in a medium-flow range, and 80 percent accurate in a low-flow range, the conventional wisdom would average the three accuracies, which would equal 90 percent, and recommend repair. If a demand profile indicates that the flow rate never drops below 1,000 gpm, however, the in-service meter accuracy for the subject application would equal 100 percent, because all flow is occurring in a high flow range. With the advantage of a demand profile, costly and unnecessary service interruption and repair costs can be avoided. Proper check valve operation in a compound meter setting can also be evaluated by ensuring that the turbine side does not move unless the small-flow side exceeds a specified flow rate.

Water meters, like any piece of machinery, have optimum performance ranges, and projected test requirements can be related to a user's demand profile. If a 4-in. meter is constantly being driven at a flow rate close to its high-end performance rating, more frequent repair requirements can be anticipated.

REFERENCE

Edgar, T. 1995. *Large Water Meter Handbook*, first ed. Dillsboro, N.C.: Flow Measurement Publishing.

This page intentionally blank.

Chapter **4**

Estimating Demands Using Fixture Values

INTRODUCTION

To properly size water taps, meters, and service lines, it is essential to know the peak demands likely to be called for by the end users. This problem was investigated during the 1920s and 1930s by Dr. Roy B. Hunter, a research physicist at the National Bureau of Standards. Using principles of probability, Hunter (1940) produced a single chart (commonly referred to as Hunter's Curve), for determining the design load in gallons per minute (gpm) expected from any combination of end users. Prior to this development, there was no uniformity among plumbing codes with respect to estimating the demand load for the water service or sizing the building water distribution system. Hunter's method was widely accepted throughout the United States and is currently the design methodology for all US model plumbing codes.

Hunter's analysis was based on the binomial distribution, a probability model that considers trials with two outcomes. In the case of a plumbing fixture, it is either on or off. Fixtures having the greatest load-bearing effect on the plumbing system were chosen to develop probability data—namely the flush-valve toilet, the flush-tank toilet, and the bathtub. The probability data were dependent on three factors particular to each kind of fixture: (1) the average duration of flow when the fixture is operating, (2) the average flow rate during actual operation, and (3) the average time between successive operations. Time considerations for successive operations were based on the assumption that the fixtures would be operating under *congested service*. This assumes that there are multiple users for the same fixture. When one user is finished, another user begins so that each fixture is continuously occupied. The times selected for successive operation of each fixture were five minutes for toilets and thirty minutes for the bathtub. The development of the probability model also established a standard for satisfactory service. Hunter's curves reflect a 99 percent confidence level; that is, there is only a one percent chance that the actual demand load will exceed the peak load estimated from the design chart.

As a result of these considerations, probability curves were generated for each fixture by plotting the number of fixtures against probable demand. The tendency in practice was to sum the probable demands of individual fixtures derived from their respective curves. Hunter recognized that would result in overestimating demands and consequently over-sizing pipes. The fault stemmed not in the probability function itself, but in incorrect estimation of the probability of *different kinds* of fixtures operating simultaneously. Instead of complicating the probability model to take into account the probable simultaneous operation of different kinds of fixtures, Hunter ingeniously employed a *weighted* solution. This means that the two lesser curves (flush-tank toilets and bathtubs) were weighted relative to the greater curve (flush-valve toilet). The weights were based on an arbitrary scale of one to ten, denoted as *fixture units,* with the flush-valve toilet assigned the greatest value. Each fixture thus weighted relative to the flush-valve toilet caused the probability curves to collapse toward the flush-valve toilet curve for the utility of a single design curve for mixed systems. For design purposes, two families of curves were recommended: Curve 1 for systems where flush-valve toilets predominate and Curve 2 where flush-tank toilets predominate.

The use of weighting, or fixture units, allowed further solutions for different building occupancies by modifying the fixture-unit value itself. For example, Hunter used field observations made in two hotels in New York City and a large apartment house in Washington, D.C., where it was observed that not more than 75 percent of the bathrooms were occupied and in use at one time. Furthermore, when considering the bathroom group as serving only one person at a time, no more than two thirds of the total number of fixtures in the bathroom group will be in use at the same time. Therefore, fixture units for multi-dwelling buildings were reduced to two thirds of 75 percent, or 50 percent of the standard weights for fixtures under congested service. This refinement introduced a distinction in fixture units between public and private plumbing systems. Although this did not eliminate the potential of overestimating peak water demand for all building-type applications, it did alert the engineer toward possible solutions.

Hunter's original probability design factors reflect good engineering judgment for water use habits in the mid-1900s. Over time, however, these factors have become outdated, especially since the 1992 federal Energy Policy Act (EPAct) mandated water-use reductions in plumbing fixtures, and now green plumbing codes require further water conservation measures. Furthermore, there is a wider variety of building types with differing fixture-use patterns that require a revision of the design chart.

By the early 1970s, there was a growing consensus among practicing engineers that, in most building types, the application of Hunter's method resulted in overdesign of the water supply system. There were two main reasons for the overly conservative design. First, the assumption of congested service often did not hold and, second, the flow rates based on plumbing fixtures from the 1930s did not apply to the new generation of water conserving fixtures in modern plumbing systems. In 1973, a US national committee commissioned through the National Academy of Sciences formed a counterpart commission to participate in the International Council for Building Research on Water Supply and Drainage for Buildings (CIB W-62) in order to address this issue. While annual symposia are still ongoing, and numerous international research projects have been published, there have been no concrete recommendations for plumbing code revisions. There has been a missing connective link between this international think tank and plumbing code development bodies. Researchers have pursued two different paths of work to address these issues, however. One course of action taken by plumbing-code development committees is to continue on the path of Hunter by further modifying the fixture-unit values and adding additional building-occupancy types. These modifications have often been made on engineering judgment rather than from observable data, resulting in a disparity among fixture-unit values between the model plumbing codes (Cole 2012)[*]. The greatest modification resulting in a substantial decrease in estimated demand is seen in the National Standard Plumbing Code (NSPC), which was also partially reproduced with modification in the Uniform Plumbing Code (UPC) as an alternate plumbing system (Appendix C, 2012). Fixture units for dwelling units are listed by bathroom groups rather than individual fixtures. Applying the NSPC modification to a 100-unit dwelling gives an estimated demand approximately 70 percent less than the demand derived from Hunter's original fixture-unit values (see Table 4-1).

AWWA is developing a new way to collect empirical measurements to generate a family of demand curves to replace the demand curves generated by Hunter's fixture-unit approach. The 1975 edition of AWWA M22 presented a family of curves that were derived from field measurements in the United States and Canada. Mechanical data loggers were used to collect peak-flow readings for a range of customers. This information was used to create a family of demand curves for several customer categories, including residential, apartments, hotels, commercial, and public facilities (schools, hospitals, etc.) (see Figures 4-1 through 4-3). To create the curves, the sum of all fixture flow rates (known as *fixture values*) in a given building were plotted against actual measured peak flow rates. Fixture values represent the peak flow in gallons per minute of each fixture or appliance when it is operated without the interference of other fixtures.

A regression curve was created that best fit the data for selected building types, showing the probable maximum flow from fixtures operating at the same time (y-axis, peak demand) against the sum demand of all fixtures (x-axis). Three families of curves were recommended: one for a residential subdivision, one for commercial and institutional uses, and another for permanent and transient dwellings. The shortcomings of the 1975 M22 curves are that they were based on a limited sample of customers and are outdated because measurements were taken before 1992 EPAct compliance.

In the last few years, there has been a greater emphasis on improving the methodology for estimating peak demands in new buildings, especially when considering LEED building designs and the growing number of water-saving fixtures and water-conservation measures required by green plumbing codes now widely adopted across the United States. Water conservation regulations promulgated in response to drought and reduced water resources availability also encourage both new and retrofitted plumbing fixtures to be used in residential and commercial applications. Some utilities have advocated a return to a modified version of the Hunter curve, whereas others have favored newer and more advanced methodologies.

---

[*] A possible exception is the National Standard Plumbing Code (NSPC). The modifications implemented in the NSPC were derived from years of collaborative research and development by Thomas Konen from the Stevens Institute of Technology. Due to an untimely death and lack of retrieval of his revision work by the NSPC committee, there is no existent rationale for the modified fixture units adopted by the NSPC.

Table 4-1 Comparative peak-flow demand for 100-unit apartment

No.	Fixture Type	2004 AWWA M22 FV	1940 Hunter FU	2012 UPC Appendix C FU	2012 IPC Appendix E FU	2012 NSPC FU
100	Toilet - Tank Type	400	—	—	—	—
100	Bathtub	800	—	—	—	—
100	Lavatory	150	—	—	—	—
100	Bathroom Groups*	—	600	350	360	102.5
Total FV or FU		**1350**	**600**	**350**	**360**	**102.5**
Estimated GPM		**68**	**142**	**95**	**97**	**45**

(100-Unit Apartment Dwelling)

*The 2004 AWWA M22 method distinguishes between flows from different fixtures while the other approaches lump them into bathroom groups.

NOTE: FV = fixture valve; FU = fixture unit

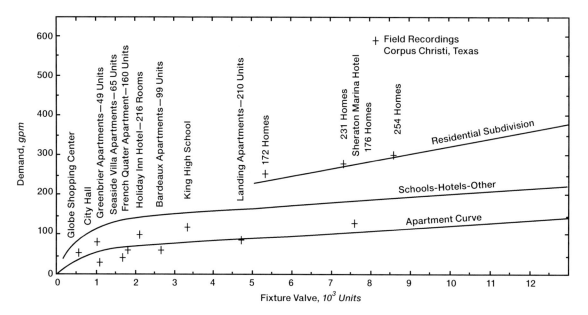

Figure 4-1 Peak-flow demand of typical customer categories

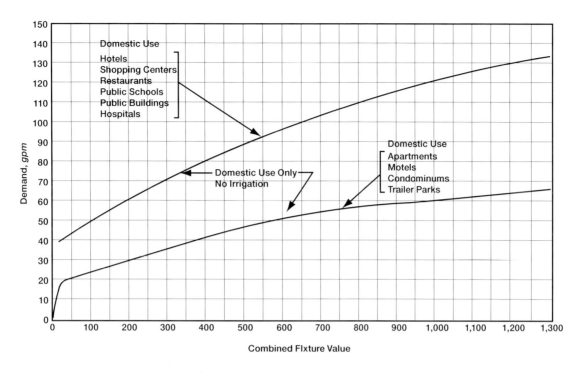

Figure 4-2   Water-flow demand per fixture value—enlarged scale from Figure 4-1

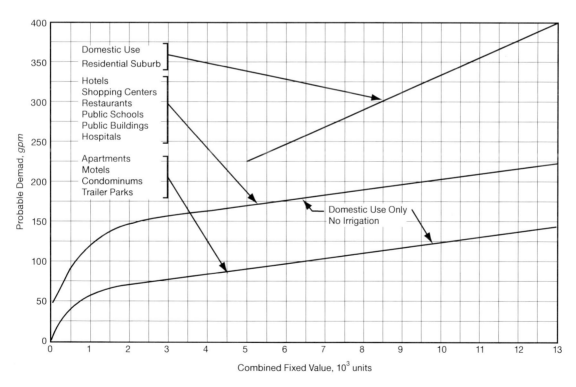

Figure 4-3   Water-flow demand per fixture value

Data collected from studies conducted during 1995 through 1999 using the type of portable data loggers described in chapter 3 have shown that the 1975 M22 curves still appear to match observed demands fairly well, with a reasonable margin of safety. By the same token, the fixture-unit modification pertaining to bathroom groups in multi-family dwelling units employed by the model codes approach the observed demands as well. By substantially reducing fixture-unit values, the demand estimate approaches the lower end of Hunter's Curve.

An example comparing peak flow predicted by the 1940 Hunter curves with the original fixture unit values, the 2004 M22 curves, and the three model plumbing codes with modified fixture units is given in Table 4-1. The comparison is made by using an example of a 100-unit apartment dwelling and considering bathroom groups only. The M22 fixture values are based on Table 4-2 (2004), the Hunter fixture units are based on Table 7 (bathroom group) in Report BMS-65 (the original 1940 Hunter report), and the model codes fixture units are a reduction of the original Hunter values. The estimated demand for the M22 fixture values is derived from Figure 4-3 using the apartment curve, and for the model codes is derived from the original Hunter curve for flush tanks. The comparison in Table 4-1 demonstrates that these different approaches have substantially reduced the estimated demand from that of the original Hunter estimation.

New Developments

Progress continues to be made toward updating design curves for plumbing systems in new building structures. Furthermore, either a reduction factor or alternate curves need to be considered where building structures exceed federal requirements (thus reducing flow rates)

Table 4-2   Examples of typical fixture values based on tested pressures

Fixture or Appliance	Fixture Value, *gpm at rated psi*
Toilet (flush valve 1.28 gpf and 1.6 gpf)	24 @ 80 psi
Toilet (flush tank)	6 @ 80 psi
Urinal (flush valve 0.5 gpf and 1.0 gpf)	10 @ 80 psi
Bidet	2
Shower (single head)	2.5 @ 80 psi
Faucet (lavatory)	1.5 @ 60 psi
Faucet (kitchen sink)	1.8 @ 60 psi
Faucet (utility sink)	4
Dishwasher	1.3 @ 35 psi
Bathtub	8
Clothes washer (vertical axis)	3–6 @ 35 psi
Clothes washer (horizontal axis)	3 @ 35 psi
Silcocks and hose bibs (with 50 ft of hose)	
^{3}/4 in.	12
Miscellaneous	
Bedpan washers	10
Drinking fountains	2
Dental units	2

when complying with state-adopted Green codes. With respect to the Hunter method, instead of arbitrarily modifying fixture units, a probability function, whether binomial or other, needs to be developed from a method that will mathematically model the empirical data to determine realistic demands.

To help reach these research goals, utilities of different size and location are needed to participate with AWWA in data logger and/or advanced metering infrastructure flow monitoring. The goal would be to collect time-of-day water use data from a select number of the most significant commercial and multi-family residential customers that comply with the 1992 EPAct. Seven subcategories of customers would include multi-family dwellings, hotels and motels, laundromats, office buildings, restaurants, food stores, and schools. Additional data needed includes an inventory of all water-using fixtures and appliances with their average and peak flow rates, the size of the building in square footage, the building occupancy number, the meter type and size, the water service size, and the pressure at the main. The data collection would encompass predicted peak-demand timeframes over a two-year period to capture seasonality. Recent data sets will enable the categorization of customers driving water demand and determine appropriate meter sizing, typical peak periods of demand, annual demand patterns, and an appropriate sampling size to develop new demand versus fixture value curves.

Methodoligies for Meter Sizing

Pending the collection and analysis of new peak-demand versus fixture-value data, some utilities use variations of the M22 methodology by developing their own service connection and water meter–sizing criteria. Denver Water, for example, requires that the meter size be the same as the tap on the water main. All components of the service line, including corporation stop, curb stop, and meter yoke are the same size. The customer generally decides what the service size should be, although the utility prefers the service size to be the minimum that will provide for the peak demand at a water velocity of 10 ft/sec or less. The minimum tap size is ¾ in. For residences with fire sprinkler systems under NFPA 13D, Denver Water allows service through the existing domestic meter. This adds 26 gpm to the domestic flow rate. To provide for this higher flow, the utility allows a velocity of 20 ft/sec under sprinkler fire demand conditions.

The City of Phoenix Water Services Department has adopted meter-sizing criteria based on the UPC (2006) and the International Residential Code (2006). The meter size depends on the maximum allowable flow in gpm and plumbing fixtures as required by the two codes based on whether the toilets are flush-valve type or flush-tank type.

The City of Tucson Water Department has adopted water-meter sizing guidelines for new development based on UPC Fixture Units and International Plumbing Code (IPC) Fixture Units, assuming the use of flush-tank toilet fixtures. The maximum meter design capacity is prescribed for meter sizes ⅝ in. through 6 in., as shown in Figure 4-5.

Guidelines for the M22 approach to determine peak demands in existing and new buildings are provided in the next section using the modified fixture-value method. This procedure is based on the fixture value approach from the 1975 Manual M22. In some situations, when usage in a facility may be uncertain, the estimated peak demand may need to be increased and the tap and service line sized accordingly. The size of the tap and service line could be larger than the meter because the cost to replace the service line will be significant. Both the service line and meter must be sized to avoid excessive head loss and must also include all minor losses (see chapter 5).

City of Phoenix
Development Services Department

WATER METER SIZING

[X] TECHNICAL GUIDELINE   [ ] INTERPRETATION   [ ] MODIFICATION

ISSUE DATE:	JULY 16, 2007
CODE/SECTION:	2006 Uniform Plumbing Code (UPC) 610.1, 2006 IRC P2903.1
APPROVED:	Tom Wandrie, P.E., Building Official
DEVELOPED BY:	Development Services Staff
REFERENCES:	C.O.P. Design Standards Manual, A.S.P.E. 1999 Plumbing Systems Chapter 5

POLICY Water meters shall be sized in accordance with the following table. The columns list the <u>maximum</u> allowable gallons per minute (gpm) and associated water supply fixture units allowed for any given meter size and type. Project designs which exceed the listed gpm unit values must be upsized to the next larger meter.

Column 1	Column 2	Column 3		Column 4	
METER SIZE & DESCRIPTION	**WSD & DSD MAXIMUM ALLOWABLE G.P.M.**	**MAXIMUM FLUSH TANK FIXTURE UNITS**		**MAXIMUM FLUSH VALVE FIXTURE UNITS**	
		UPC	IRC	UPC	IRC
5/8" x 3/4" PD	15	21	10	0	5
3/4" x 3/4" PD	25	42	35	8	9
1" PD	40	86		28	
1-1/2" PD	65	200		92	
2" PD	100	380		245	
2" COMPOUND	128	522		416	
3" COMPOUND	250	1335		1335	
4" COMPOUND	400	2670		2670	
6" COMPOUND	800	6280		6280	
8" COMPOUND	1280	10,048		10,048	
2" TURBO	128				
3" TURBO	280				
4" TURBO	480				
6" TURBO	1000				
8" TURBO	2080				

NOTES FOR TABLE USE

1. **Column 1** identifies meter sizes and types available from the City of Phoenix. (PD = Positive Displacement) The use of turbo water meters may be limited. Note: Use of water meters 6-inches and larger requires special advance consultation with Water Services to determine availability, actual flow capacity, meter cost, and delivery schedule.

2. **Column 2** is the design meter flow rate as determined by the Water Services and the Development Services Departments.

3. **Column 3** is the maximum number of fixture units permitted on a meter when the plumbing fixtures are predominantly flush tank type water closets and urinals. Valves based on 2006 Uniform Plumbing Code (UPC) and 2006 International Residential Code (IRC), whichever is applicable.

4. **Column 4** is the maximum number of fixture units permitted on a water meter when the plumbing fixtures are predominantly flush valve type water closets and urinals, based on 2006 UPC and 2006 IRC, whichever is applicable

Figure 4-4   City of Phoenix meter-sizing criteria

Courtesy of City of Phoenix

Some water utilities allow a customer's designated engineer to select the meter size, and frequently they do not allow more than one size reduction from the service line diameter. It is recommended that utilities that allow such a meter-size reduction require the engineer to present an analysis of head loss and the associated implications. As noted later in this chapter, irrigation demands should be separately metered where possible and warranted.

Where base-load continuous demands are present or intermittent irrigation demands occur, these demands must be considered in meter and service-line sizing. Irrigation demands that will occur simultaneously with peak domestic demands must be added to the domestic demands. Where irrigation demands normally occur during off-peak domestic-use times, the controlling peak demand should be the larger of the two. Where continuous demands, such as cooling loads, occur, these must also be added to the peak domestic demands.

USING THE MODIFIED FIXTURE-VALUE METHOD

Domestic Demands

Although all plumbing codes contain the Hunter method for estimating the water demand load for the building plumbing system, not all plumbing codes regulate how the water-service demand load should be calculated. For example, the IPC and the NSPC only contain general statements requiring the water service to be adequately sized for the quantities and pressures required in the code and to have a minimum size of ¾-in. in diameter. The UPC only contains provisions estimating the demand and pipe sizes for the building water-distribution system after the water meter. However, the Illinois and Wisconsin plumbing codes regulate water-service sizing based on the Hunter method.

The most prevalent recommended procedures for estimating demand loads found in plumbing codes for building water supply pipe sizing were originally published by the National Bureau of Standards in *Water-Distributing Systems for Buildings, Report BMS-79* (Hunter 1941) and the *Plumbing Manual, Report BMS-66* (1940). These procedures are placed in the appendices of the model plumbing codes and are not mandatory unless adopted by the municipality. The procedures are still sound even though the original tables are acknowledged to be outdated.

There are two types of demands that need to be considered for the water service; domestic or indoor water demand and landscape irrigation demand. The following steps are M22 guidelines for estimating the water demand from domestic use by plumbing fixtures and appliances. Most types of fixtures and uses are included to permit the water engineer to estimate the probable use of residential, public, office, schools, shopping centers, and other customers. The criteria as set out, however, will not ensure that the user will not exceed the estimated demand. The engineer should thoroughly evaluate the customer's future demand and piping before reaching a conclusion.

An example for estimating the probable domestic demand for a hypothetical apartment complex with a working pressure at the meter outlet of 80 psi is presented in Table 4-4. This demand is calculated as approximately 85 gpm.

Fixture values. The first step is to calculate the demand from fixture values by listing all of the proposed plumbing fixtures with their appropriate fixture values (FV), as shown in Table 4-4. As defined in the 1975 M22, a fixture value (as opposed to a fixture unit used by Hunter) is simply the best estimate of the peak instantaneous demand of a given fixture or appliance, depending on circumstances and based on the actual conditions at its point of use. This parameter was arbitrarily chosen to serve as a simple variable against which measured peak demands could be plotted in order to develop demand probability curves. Fixture values represent the peak flow in gallons per minute of each fixture or appliance when it is operated without the interference of other fixtures. The assumed peak flow is based on the manufacturer's listed maximum flow rate according to the fixture's standard testing pressure. For example, a lavatory faucet listed with a maximum flow rate of 1.5 gpm is based on a testing pressure of 60 psi. Some suggested fixture values have been provided in Table 4-2 and Figure 4-5. The user is reminded that these are only suggested values for domestic-type uses at the listed test pressures, and actual demands for the fixtures and appliances being used in the proposed building should be utilized. Actual values should be used when considering the residual pressure at the fixture outlet. For example, the listed performance of high-efficiency kitchen faucets is 1.8 gpm at a pressure of 60 psi. The flow rate begins to diminish at lesser pressures. If the actual building plumbing system pressure during peak loads leaves a residual pressure of 15 psi for the faucet, the listed performance will be reduced to 1 gpm (see Figure 4-6 and Table 4-3). Therefore, the fixture value will need to be adjusted accordingly.

Pressure adjustment. To obtain a more accurate fixture value, the pressure available at the fixture outlet could be estimated in order to derive the fixture flow. The pressure available at the meter outlet may not necessarily be the same pressure available at the fixture outlet. In most cases, it is not. The pressure available at the fixture outlet is the residual pressure remaining after head loss due to pipe friction, minor losses, and elevation changes. The engineer would need to determine the extent of calculating residual pressure at fixtures and appliances for fixture value adjustments. Practically, residual pressures could be calculated for each floor level, taking into account head pressure and the average friction loss due to piping and appurtenances.

Meter Size (inches)	Maximum UPC Fixture Units[1] ()	Maximum IPC Fixture Units[2] ()	Tucson Water Maximum Meter Design Capacity (gpm)
5/8	20	11	15
3/4	35	28	22½
1	78	78	37½
1½	250	250	75
2	480	480	120
3	1530	1530	270
4	3470	3470	475
6	8900	8900	1050

NOTES:
1. Fixture unit limits were interpolated from Appendix A of the 2006 Uniform Plumbing code (UPC) and assume the use of the flush tanks.
2. Fixture unit limits were interpolated from Table E103.3(3) of the International Plumbing Code (IPC) and assume the use of flush tanks.
3. For meter sizes larger than 6" consult New Services.

Figure 4-5   City of Tucson meter-sizing criteria

Courtesy of Tucson Water

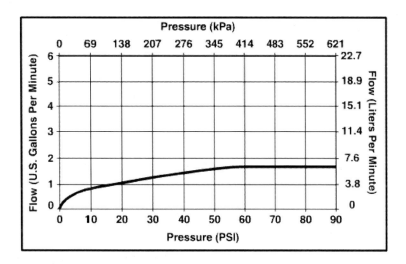

Figure 4-6   Example of a kitchen faucet flow chart
Courtesy of Delta Faucet Company

If a more accurate fixture value is desired, the second step is to adjust the fixture value by applying a pressure adjustment to the fixture's baseline maximum flow rate. Table 4-3 shows an example of a fixture value adjustment for a kitchen faucet listed at a maximum flow rate of 1.8 gpm at 60 psi. The table was created from the flow chart for the faucet in Figure 4-6. Similar flow charts for other fixtures can be provided by the manufacturer. If the residual pressure at the fixture is 25 psi, the fixture value will be adjusted to 1.2. A pressure adjustment factor of 0.67 can be applied to all similar faucets having the same residual pressure where flow charts are not obtainable. For instance, the pressure adjustment factor of 0.67 could also be applied to a 1.5-gpm lavatory faucet with marginal error.

Demand. The third step after the total adjusted fixture values have been determined is to apply the results to the demand curves, such as shown in Figures 4-2 or 4-3. Similar curves developed by a qualified engineer with locally obtained data or data from similar structures elsewhere should be considered by the utility. Notice that the demand curves are not linear. The reason for this pattern is that the accumulated maximum flow of one fixture type will always be greater than many fixture types concurrently operating in service. That is, the probability of all fixtures operating at one time diminishes as the number of fixtures or appliances increases. It is also critical to note that a fixture value in different types of customers will have different impacts on peak demands. The current figures include only three curves: one for residential suburbs; one for various commercial and institutional uses; and one for apartments, condominiums, motels, and trailer parks. Additional curves for more specific types of customers could be developed from new empirical research. The demands for supermarkets, office buildings, restaurants, and high schools could be separate curves altogether.

The last step is to add the demand from hose bibs to the probable demand determined by the demand curves. Loads from hose bibs are considered continuous demand and not subject to probability and, therefore, must be added to the probable demand.

Table 4-4 indicates a sample domestic demand calculation for a hypothetical apartment complex. The fixture values are from examples in Table 4-2 based on manufacturer's testing standards. The adjusted fixture values are hypothetical residual pressure adjustments. At the bottom of Table 4-4, calculated demand from an assumed single hose bib is indicated and added to the domestic demand.

Table 4-3   Example of fixture value adjustment for pressure (based on Figure 4-6)

	Kitchen Faucet Fixture Value Adjustment		
Residual Pressure at Fixture Outlet, *psi*	Baseline Flow Rate at 60 *psi*	Actual Flow Rate at Residual Pressure (Fixture Value)	Pressure Adjustment Factor
15	1.8	1.0	0.56
20	1.8	1.1	0.61
25	1.8	1.2	0.67
30	1.8	1.3	0.72
35	1.8	1.4	0.78
40	1.8	1.5	0.83
50	1.8	1.7	0.94
60	1.8	1.8	1.00
70	1.8	1.8	1.00
80	1.8	1.8	1.00

Table 4-4   Sample apartment domestic demand calculation

Sample Probable Domestic Demand Calculation Hypothetical Apartment Complex (Meter Outlet Pressure = 80 psi)				
Step 1. List the fixture values				
Step 2. Calculate FV adjustments based on residual pressure at fixture outlet				
Fixtures/Appliances	Number	Fixture Value *gpm*	Adjusted Fixture Value *gpm*	Total Fixture Value *gpm*
Toilets (tank)	205	6	2.5	512.5
Faucets (lavatory)	259	1.5	1.2	310.8
Dishwashers	138	1.3*	2.0	276
Clothes washers	10	3	3.0	30
Faucets (kitchen)	165	1.8	1.0	165
Bathtubs	162	8	8.0	1,296
Showers	162	2.5	2.1	340.2
			Total Fixture Value	2,930.5

Step 3. Apply total fixture value to demand curve

Demand (gpm) from Fig. 4.3	**76 gpm**

Step 4. Add in demand for hose bibs
    (Number of hose bibs) × (Fixture value at 60 psi is 9 gpm)
    In this example there is only one hose bib, therefore: 1 × 9 =   **9 gpm**
    Total probable demand
    Add demand from step 3 and step 4   **85 gpm**

* Fixture value is based on nominal pressure of 35 psi, so adjusted fixture value increases in this case for the meter outlet pressure of 80 psi.

* Based on recommendation from the Irrigation Association to ensure flow velocity does not exceed 7.5 ft/sec.

* Values based on a service line flow rate not exceeding 7.5 ft/sec.

**Assumes 100% turf and overhead irrigation to include spray or rotor type sprinklers. Larger landscape areas can be served if irrigation system flows are lowered with drip and micro-spray.

Irrigation Demand

Turf irrigation represents one of the largest water demands by the utility customer. Large amounts of water in excess of domestic use are often required, thereby necessitating particular care in calculating the irrigation demand. If irrigation demand is underestimated, there can be insufficient pressure available to operate domestic fixtures during turf irrigation.

A separate irrigation meter is desirable in many areas because wastewater charges are typically based on water use. If that use includes irrigation (which does not contribute to wastewater flows), a customer could end up paying wastewater charges on a much higher volume than necessary. Using a dedicated irrigation meter provides useful information on specific irrigation demands and ensures that unnecessary charges for wastewater are avoided.

In California, a separate irrigation meter is required for any commercial landscape that is larger than 5,000 ft^2. Single-family residential services are exempted from this requirement. There is no harm in installing a dedicated irrigation meter with an approved backflow prevention device at sites where irrigation is practiced, regardless of the landscape size. The basic rule of thumb established through previous editions of Manual M22 is to recommend a separate meter serving irrigation for any landscape (commercial or residential) larger than 15,000 ft^2. Requiring a separate irrigation meter for smaller landscapes, as is practiced in California, is perfectly acceptable.

Automatic sprinkler systems can and should be programmed to operate during periods of off-peak domestic demands (from late night to early morning). This is even more important if a single meter is used to serve both domestic and irrigation demands. It is recommended that the full irrigation demand not be simply added to the peak domestic demand to calculate the maximum design demand for the customer. Therefore, where the irrigation system is governed by an automatic controller, the controlling demand for design should normally be the larger of the domestic demand or the irrigation demand. For manual irrigation systems, the demand from at least one garden hose should be included as part of the peak demand.

Manual Irrigation and End-of-Hose Sprinklers

In many homes, particularly in older residential areas, the resident supplies the lawn-watering needs manually from sill cocks located on the outside wall of the building and from yard-hose bibs. The sill cocks usually are connected to a ½-in. or ¾-in. supply pipe, and the use of these outlets has a direct effect on water pressures within the house. Hoses that connect the sprinkler to the hose bib vary from ⅜-in. to ¾-in. in diameter and generally govern the rate of flow due to friction loss. Sprinklers can be obtained in a wide range of water-flow capacities and types, which makes detailed estimation of peak demand difficult.

Flow tests under actual field conditions have been made on a ring sprinkler that will provide the water engineer or estimator with a general basis for an average of portable-sprinkler water conditions at various pressures. The flow variation through 50 ft of ⅝-in. diameter hose and a brass ring sprinkler fed by a 1½-in. house service and a ¾-in. lateral to a ¾-in. sill cock is as shown in Figure 4-7.

Basic Line Sizing for Automatic Irrigation Systems

The Irrigation Association (IA) recommends that the flow velocity through the service line for an automatic irrigation system not exceed 7.5 ft/sec (IA 2012, 2013). This requirement effectively limits the size of landscape that can be adequately served through service lines of different sizes. The velocity of flow through the service line becomes the critical limiting factor.

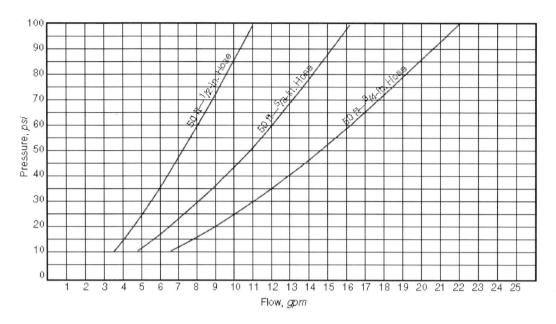

Figure 4-7   Variations in flow from garden hoses due to pressure changes

There are several approaches for sizing dedicated irrigation service lines. The method presented herein was developed in conjunction with the IA and offers a rule-of-thumb approach to irrigation meter sizing based on the landscape area that will be served by the irrigation meter. This method provides a simple method for determining if a landscape area can be adequately irrigated through a meter and service line of a designated size. While not intended as a replacement for other, customized meter-sizing methods, this approach can be used to confirm right sizing of irrigation meters and service lines.

Using the method developed by the IA, the peak daily demand is determined and then adjusted based on the chosen irrigation interval, such as every two days, three days, four days etc., and a watering window during which irrigation needs to be completed. As the length of the irrigation interval increases, the size of the water tap required also increases. For the purposes of this manual, a two-day irrigation interval was assumed.

The flow rate required to provide sufficient water to meet the peak-day irrigation demand can be calculated using equation 4-1:

$$Q = \frac{ET_O \times K_L \times I_N \times A \times 0.623}{(Hours \times 60) \times IE} \qquad \text{(Eq. 4-1)}$$

Where:

Q = Flow rate of water in gpm

ET_O = Grass reference evapotranspiration in in./d (use peak demand day)

K_L = Landscape coefficient to modify ET_O. For planning purposes, use 0.70.

I_N = Irrigation interval in number of days

A = Area in ft^2

0.623 = Conversion from in.-ft^2 to gal

$Hours$ = Hours in water window to accomplish the irrigation for peak demand

60 = Conversion from hr to min

IE = Irrigation efficiency. For planning purposes, use 0.75.

The result will show the flow rate in gpm to irrigate the landscape area (*A*) during peak demand based on the watering window and interval for watering days, i.e., 10 hr, for the water window, and watering days are every other day.

Irrigation efficiency (*IE*) is determined by comparing water beneficially used to water applied. This accounts for sprinkler distribution uniformity and irrigation management skill. It also accounts for water that is delivered but lands off target or is excessively applied and becomes runoff or deep percolation. It is suggested that 0.70–0.80 be used as the typical irrigation efficiency for permanently installed sprinklers. While the use of drip irrigation will have a higher potential efficiency, for the purposes of planning, a target irrigation efficiency of 0.75 is acceptable. For reference, the California Model Efficient Landscape Water Ordinance uses *IE* = 0.71 for irrigation efficiency. Most references that focus on agricultural irrigation will use irrigation efficiency of approximately 0.75 for solid set (permanent) irrigation sprinklers.

Equation 4-1 can be rearranged to solve for area as shown in equation 4-2. This enables the calculation of a specific landscape size that can be served by a meter and service line with a designated flow capacity.

$$A = \frac{Q \times (Hours \times 60) \times IE}{ET_O \times K_L \times I_N \times 0.623} \qquad \text{(Eq. 4-2)}$$

To ensure proper functioning and long-term reliability of in-ground irrigation systems, the IA recommends that *Q* be set such that the flow velocity in the system never exceeds 7.5 ft/sec. This becomes an important limiting factor in the size of the service line.

By assuming a 100 percent turf landscape in a hot and dry region, to be watered by overhead irrigation including spray or rotor-type sprinklers, it is possible to develop reasonable estimates of the maximum landscape size that can be adequately served through service lines of different sizes. Table 4-5 shows the results of this analysis. Typically, water meters connected to these service lines will be the same size or one size smaller than the service line. Please note that this table is not intended to replace a customized meter and line sizing calculation that is site-specific. Rather, Table 4-5 provides a simple check on irrigation meter sizing that can be used to help water providers ensure proper flow and velocity within an irrigation system.

Landscaped areas larger than those listed in Table 4-5 can be served if irrigation system flows are lowered. Flows can easily be lowered through the use of drip and microspray as well as low-precipitation–rate sprinkler heads. Key assumptions in this table include the ET_O that is set at 0.5 in./d and I_N that is set to every two days. This suggests a very hot and dry climate, where 0.5 in. of supplemental irrigation water is required every two days (2.5 in. of irrigation per week). Very few climates in North America ever exceed this requirement, so this approaches a "worst case" sizing scenario. Adjusting the factors assumed here for local conditions allows this method to be tailored to meet the specific demands of an irrigation system in a particular climate zone.

Table 4-5   Service line size and maximum irrigated turf area

Service Line Size *in.*	Q = Max. Recommended Continuous Flow Rate, *gpm**	Hours = Maximum Allowed Hours for Irrigation Per Day	I_N = Irrigation Interval, *days*	ET_O (high) = Max. Irrigation Requirement Based on Climate *in./d*	Max. Irrigated Turf Area $ft^{2\dagger}$	Max. Irrigated Turf Area acres[†]
⅝	7	14	2	0.5	10,112	0.2
¾	10	14	2	0.5	14,446	0.3
1	17	14	2	0.5	24,559	0.6
1.25	27	14	2	0.5	39,005	0.9
1.5	37	14	2	0.5	53,451	1.2
2	65	14	2	0.5	93,900	2.2
2.5	100	14	2	0.5	144,462	3.3
3	155	14	2	0.5	223,917	5.1

* Values based on service line flow rate not to exceed 7.5 ft/sec.

† Assumes 100% turf and overhead irrigation to include spray or rotor type sprinklers. Larger landscape areas can be served if irrigation system flows are lowered with drip and micro-spray.

REFERENCES

Cole, D. 2012. *Determining Fixture Units for High-Efficiency Fixtures.* Ontario, Calif.: International Association of Plumbing and Mechanical Officials.

Hunter, R. 1940. *Methods of Estimating Loads in Plumbing Systems,* Report BMS65, Washington, D.C.: National Bureau of Standards.

Hunter, R. 1941. Water Distributing Systems for Buildings, Report BMS79. Washington D.C.: United States Government Printing Office.

International Association of Plumbing and Mechanical Officials (IAPMO). 2012. Uniform Plumbing Code (UPC). Ontario, CA: IAPMO.

IAPMO. 2012. International Plumbing Code (IPC). Ontario, CA: IAPMO.

IAPMO. 2012. National Standard Plumbing Code (NSPC). Ontario, CA: IAPMO.

IAPMO. 2006. International Residential Code. Ontario, CA: IAPMO.

Irrigation Association (IA). 2012. Standard for Automatic Irrigation Systems. Fall Church, VA: IA.

Irrigation Association. 2014. *Landscape Irrigation Best Management Practices.* Fall Church, VA: IA and American Society of Irrigation Consultants.

Plumbing Manual, *Report of Subcommittee on Plumbing of the Central Housing Committee on Research, Design, and Construction.* 1940. Report BMS-66. Washington, D.C.: National Bureau of Standards.

Chapter **5**

Sizing Service Lines

INTRODUCTION

This chapter describes how to determine the size of water service lines and valves given the design flow rate and head available at the main. The determination of service line size is more conservative than the determination of meter size, because the service line size must accommodate local water system operational limitations. In addition, there is a substantial cost associated with replacing a service line. The methodologies described cover a wide array of problems from sizing a single-family residence's service line to sizing large industrial and commercial services with fire hydrants and sprinklers. The chapter will not describe the sizing of customer plumbing, although some consideration of a customer's plumbing is necessary, especially when the system includes sprinklers and hydrants.

All customer situations have similar challenges. Only a limited amount of head is available in the main. Selecting larger-diameter service lines and appurtenances results in greater capacity services but also results in higher costs than the costs of smaller lines. The goal in design is to correctly size the combination of pipes, valves, and meter to meet the customer's needs based on the best available data.

There are several ways of performing the necessary hydraulic calculations for service line sizing, ranging from hand calculations to spreadsheets to sophisticated computer models. All of these approaches require knowing the head at some point and then using some description of the relationship between flow rate and head loss to calculate the flow through the service. Each piece of data required is described in an individual section in the chapter followed by a description of how to perform the calculations.

DATA REQUIRED

Design Flow Rate

The starting point for sizing calculations is the design flow rate. This rate can be estimated (1) using the traditional fixture value method, (2) using a modified fixture unit method that incorporates up-to-date fixture units, or (3) by demand profiling existing sites. The design flow rate used in the subsequent calculations is the maximum flow rate at which the fixtures will work properly. Up-to-date fixture unit information is not generally available at this time. Ongoing research efforts are intended to correct this deficiency. In the meantime, current fixture unit information may lead to overly conservative sizing of services.

For the design of residential single-line piping for both domestic and fire sprinkler systems, both the local plumbing code and NFPA 13D standard should be consulted for the design flow rate. For a multipurpose system, the design flow rate for the service line is based on either the number of design sprinklers according to NFPA 13D, or the number of plumbing fixtures according to the plumbing code, whichever is greater.

Head

Two heads (or hydraulic grade line elevations) are used in service line sizing. The first is the head available in the main at the tap location. This head is composed of the pressure in the main combined with the elevation corresponding to that pressure. The second head is the required head at the downstream end of the service line. This head is composed of the minimum acceptable pressure and the elevation corresponding to that pressure. This head will usually correspond to the head downstream of the meter and any backflow prevention devices. The difference between the available head at the main and the required head is the acceptable head loss in the service line, meter, and valving.

Elevation of Main and Service Line

The elevation of the main is either the actual elevation of the main or the elevation of the pressure gauge attached to a nearby fire hydrant if the pressure used as the water utility pressure is measured at a hydrant. Similarly, the elevation of the customer service line is usually taken as the elevation immediately downstream of the meter, although for some situations the elevation of a particular hydrant or sprinkler on the customer's side of the meter is used. The distinction is whether the individual performing service line calculations is interested in only sizing the service lines or is sizing the complete customer plumbing system.

It is not as important to know the actual elevation of the main and the customer service line as the difference in elevations. In areas that are flat (e.g., the elevation of the main is comparable to that of the meter), the difference in elevation may be negligible, and it may be possible to simply compare the difference in pressure between the main and the customer service line.

Available Pressure

The available pressure, or head, used to start the calculation is typically taken as the working pressure under a reasonable worst-case condition (e.g., peak hour demands, fire demands, condition when nearby pump is off), which will vary from utility to utility. Normally, this value is determined by hydraulic modeling of the system. In the absence of modeling data, actual pressure measured at a nearby hydrant during a time corresponding to peak water use can also be used.

No single, correct value is available to measure pressure in the main. The problem is that the pressure in a main varies over the course of the day because of changes in water demand, pump operation, and tank water level. It also varies in the long term due to changes in pipe-carrying capacity, adjustment in pressure zone boundaries, and long-term changes in demands.

The engineer sizing the service line should check with the utility concerning expected pressure at a tie-in point in the distribution system and any planned changes in expected pressure. Utilities should be careful when discussing pressures so as not to give the impression that they are guaranteeing a specific pressure under all conditions.

Another complicating factor is that the water use through the new service may itself affect pressure. A new residential tap on a 12-in. main will not affect pressure in the main. A 6-in. tap for an industrial customer on a 6-in. main, however, may affect the available pressure depending on the strength of the distribution system in that area. When the capability of the distribution system to serve the new customer is in doubt, a fire hydrant flow test may be appropriate to assess the distribution system capacity. When the piping is not yet installed and a utility has a calibrated hydraulic model of the remainder of the system, the model may also be used to estimate pressure under a variety of future conditions. Use of a model may be necessary in a situation where the mains have not yet been laid.

Required Pressure

As with available pressure, there is no simple rule to determine the required pressure, or head, for the customer. Most customer fixtures will work over a wide range of pressures. At higher pressures, however, more flow will be delivered for a given opening of the faucet or valve. In some instances, a minimum pressure is required to enable pressure-seating valves to operate.

Some fixtures will operate at pressures as low as 5 psi; however, the UPC and NSPC require a minimum 15 psi *residual* pressure (therefore, the customer service line pressure will need to be higher). The IPC requires a minimum 8 psi for faucets and 20 psi for pressure-balanced valves (HE faucets require high pressures to meet the design flow rate). Some water-reducing fixtures today are requiring much higher pressures for performance that meets manufacturer specifications.

The height of fixtures above the service line also affects pressure. In order to provide 10 psi to a shower on the second story of a building, pressure of approximately 25 psi downstream of the meter in the basement is required. For most showers with pressure-balanced valves, the minimum pressure is 20 psi.

As for the design flow rate, the required pressure for single-line piping for both domestic and fire supply for residential fire sprinkler systems is prescribed by the NFPA 13D standard and the local plumbing code. The NFPA standard sets required flow and pressure requirements for one sprinkler head and, in most instances, for two sprinkler heads flowing simultaneously. Pressure delivered to each sprinkler head, under sprinkler flow conditions, is to be the higher of the minimum operating pressure given in the sprinkler listing, or 7 psi. The design professional will need to consult both the plumbing code and NFPA 13D for pressure requirements in a multi-purpose system.

HEAD LOSS

Maximum Allowable Head Loss

The maximum allowable head loss can be calculated as the difference between the head in the main and the head required by the customer. In US customary units, this is given by equation 5-1:

$$h_a = (z\ main - z\ cust) + 2.31\ (p\ main - p\ cust)$$ (Eq. 5-1)

Where:

h_a = maximum allowable head loss, *ft*
$z\ main$ = elevation of main, *ft*
$z\ cust$ = elevation corresponding to *p cust, ft*
$p\ main$ = pressure in main, *psi*
$p\ cust$ = pressure required by customer, *psi*
2.31 = conversion factor from psi to ft of water

It is not necessary to know the exact values of *z main* and *z cust* as long as one knows their difference.

If h_a is negative or very small (say < 5 ft), it may be possible to reevaluate and adjust some of the other parameters on the right side of the equation. Otherwise, if readjustment is not feasible, it may be necessary for the customer to install a booster pump to obtain design flow at a satisfactory pressure, being sure to maintain a suction pressure upstream of the pump of at least 5 psi. In general, pumping is only acceptable for large customers. Most utilities do not allow individual residential customers to install booster pumps. The requirement to provide 5 psi of pump suction within the customer plumbing does not supersede the requirement to maintain at least 20 psi (or more in some jurisdictions) in distribution mains.

Head Loss

It is necessary to use energy to move water from one point in the pipeline to another. The energy used cannot be recovered and is therefore "lost." In water distribution, this energy is usually reported in head (length) units, and the loss is referred to as *head loss*.

The head loss at the design flow rate must next be calculated for the piping configuration to determine if that flow can be delivered. If the available head exceeds the calculated head loss, that flow can be delivered. Methods for determining head loss for pipes, valves, and meters are discussed in the following sections.

Piping Losses

When the length of a service line is substantial, pipe head loss is the most significant component of head loss. The pipe head loss can be calculated using many different equations, including the Hazen–Williams, Darcy–Weisbach, and Manning equations. In the United States, the Hazen–Williams equation is usually used. The Hazen–Williams equation for pipe head loss is written in terms of velocity. In US customary units, this is given as equation 5-2:

$$V = 0.55\ Cd^{0.63}\ (h/L)^{0.54}$$ (Eq. 5-2)

Where:

V = velocity, *ft/sec*
C = Hazen–Williams C factor
d = diameter, *ft*
h = head loss, *ft*
L = length, *ft*

In most problems, the diameter should be expressed in inches and flow in gallons per minute instead of velocity. In this case, the equation becomes equation 5-3:

$$h = 10.4\, L\, (Q/C)^{1.85} D^{-4.87}$$ (Eq. 5-3)

Where:

Q = flow rate, *gpm*
D = pipe inside diameter, *in.*

The Hazen–Williams C factor depends on the piping material. Values of approximately 150 have been reported for plastic and copper tubing. Usually, a value of 130 is used as a conservative value for design.

For the small-size pipes used in service lines, the actual inside diameter (ID) of the pipe should be used and not the nominal diameter, because these two values can be significantly different depending on the class of pipe. Table 5-1 gives the typical ID corresponding to the nominal diameter for a variety of pipe materials and thicknesses (pressure class). Note that cross-linked polyethylene (PEX) tubing closely follows the sizing and head losses of polyethylene (PE) pipe. Commonly used PEX is SDR9 (see PE piping, per copper tubing sizing, IDR9).

For those who prefer not to calculate the head loss, tables are provided in appendix B to make it easy to determine head loss. Simply look up the head loss per unit length and multiply by the length of the pipe.

For a reasonable initial estimate of diameter on which to base sizing calculations, the diameter that results in a velocity of 5–8 ft/sec at peak design flow can be used and calculate diameter as equation 5-4.

$$D = \sqrt{Q/2.44V}$$ (Eq. 5-4)

The calculated diameter is rounded up to the next commercially available size. This value may need to be adjusted depending on the head available, number of appurtenances (e.g., meters, backflow preventers) in the line, and length of the line.

Table 5-1 Actual internal diameter versus nominal diameter

Material and Class	Nominal diameter, in.										
	¾	1	1½	2	2½	3	3½	4	5	6	8
	Actual internal diameter, in.										
Copper											
Type K	0.745	0.995	1.481	1.959	2.435	2.907	3.385	3.857	4.805	5.741	7.583
Type L	0.785	1.025	1.505	1.985	2.465	2.945	3.425	3.905	4.875	5.485	7.725
Type M	0.811	1.055	1.527	2.009	2.495	2.981	3.459	3.935	4.907	5.881	7.785
Ductile iron											
Class 50										6.400	8.510
Class 51						3.460		4.280		6.340	8.450
Class 52						3.400		4.220		6.280	8.390
Class 53						3.340		4.160		6.220	8.330
Polyethylene											
IDR9	0.681	0.875	1.263	1.653							
PVC C900											
Class 100 (DR25)								4.416		6.282	8.240
Class 150 (DR18)								4.266		6.042	7.924
Class 200 (DR14)								4.114		5.796	7.602
PVC ASTM D2241											
Class 100 (SDR41)											
Class 125 (SDR32.4)											
Class 160 (SDR26)		1.155	1.714	2.153	2.615	3.190		5.081			
Class 200 (SDR21)	0.890	1.149	1.680	2.109	2.561	3.126		4.969			
Class 250 (SDR17)	0.886	1.121	1.636	2.055	2.497	3.038		4.831			
Steel											
Schedule 40	0.824	1.049	1.610	2.067	2.469	3.068	3.548	4.026	5.047	6.065	7.981

Head Loss for Valves and Fittings

Numerous types of valves and fittings are used in service lines. Some typical valves are described in this section. Methods for determining head loss through the valves and fittings are presented in the following section. (General standards for service line valves and fittings are given in ANSI/AWWA C800. The manufacturer's specifications should also be checked.)

Corporation stopcocks. These valves are used at the service tap in the water main and are usually left fully open. They are full-bore valves that cause minimal head loss.

Gooseneck fittings. For smaller pipe diameters, the pipe is usually tapped at or near the top of the pipe, and there is a curved section of pipe called a *gooseneck*, which changes the direction of flow from the vertical to horizontal heading toward the customer. The extra head loss due to this bend is usually relatively small compared to other minor losses.

Curb stops. These valves are used to start or stop customer service. They are usually full-bore ball valves with a minimal head-loss value. An important consideration with curb stops and corporation stops is that they must be fully opened. If they are left partly opened, they can cause significant head loss. For most utilities, the curb stop marks the end of the utility's piping and the beginning of the customer's piping.

Meter yokes. Appropriate head loss values or head loss across the yoke needs to be added into the head-loss calculations.

Backflow prevention assemblies and check valves. These valves are installed to prevent backflow from the customer's plumbing into the distribution system. Their use is often mandated by building codes or state environmental regulations and is further described in Manual M14 (AWWA 2004). This group includes a variety of assemblies from simple flap check valves to fully testable reduced-pressure backflow prevention (RPBP) assemblies. These valves usually have a great deal of head loss associated with them.

Globe, angle, and gate valves. These valves are used to isolate the customer's system. They are usually intended to be fully opened or fully closed. Throttling these valves will affect the ability of the system to deliver the design flow.

Pressure-reducing valves. These valves are used to protect the customer's plumbing from excessive pressure in the distribution system. They are usually placed between the curb stop and the meter and are owned by the customer. In most cases, at design flow rate, these valves should be fully opened, because at such flow there will usually be sufficient head loss in the piping and meters that throttling the pressure is not needed. They can usually be treated as being fully opened valves. The head loss value will depend on the type of valve body (e.g., globe and angle).

Minor Losses

Minor losses refers to head losses other than through the pipe itself and includes losses caused by valves, meters, backflow prevention assemblies, bends, and changes in diameter. These losses are usually a function of the velocity (and hence flow) squared. A problem in calculating these losses is that the data are usually given in a variety of forms including:

- Minor loss, k
- Minor loss, C_v
- Curve of minor loss versus flow rate
- Equivalent pipe length
- Orifice, K

Methods for calculating minor head loss (h) given each form of data are described in the following section.

Minor loss, k. The minor loss, k, is a dimensionless number that is used to relate head loss to velocity in equation 5-5:

$$h = kV^2/2g \qquad \text{(Eq. 5-5)}$$

Where:

k = minor loss k
g = acceleration due to gravity, *ft/sec²*

Substituting flow rate for velocity in the previous equation gives Equation 5-6:

$$h = kQ^2/(383 \, D^4) \qquad \text{(Eq. 5-6)}$$

Where:

Q = flow rate, *gpm*
D = diameter, *in.*

Where the head loss is desired in psi (p), simply divide the head loss in feet by 2.31 to obtain the following:

$$p = h/2.31 \qquad \text{(Eq. 5-7)}$$

Typical k values for valves, bends, and fittings are available from a number of sources (Crane 1969; Hydraulic Institute 1978; Walski 1994) and are summarized in Table 5-2. Minor losses for meters are given in Table 5-3. The meter values are based on the maximum allowable head loss at design flow rate according to AWWA meter standards C700, C701, C702, C703, C704, C708, C710, C712, C713, C714, and C750. Actual head-loss values are usually less than those stated in the standards. They may be only slightly less for meters with strainers but are often significantly less for meters without strainers. Individual meter manufacturers' curves should be checked.

Minor loss, C_v. For certain types of valves, minor losses are usually presented in terms of a carrying capacity instead of a k-value such that:

$$h = 2.31 \, (Q/C_v)^2 \qquad \text{(Eq. 5-8)}$$

Where:

$$C_v = \text{minor loss carrying capacity, } gpm/\sqrt{psi}$$

Table 5-2 Minor loss k-values

Component	k-values
Gate Valve	
3/4 closed	24
1/2 closed	5.6
1/4 closed	1.2
Fully open	0.2
Angle valve open	2.5
Globe valve	6
Swing check	2
Angle valve	2.2
Ball check	4.5
Butterfly valve	
open	1.2
20°	1.4
40°	10
60°	94
80°	1,750
Foot valve hinged	2.2
Foot valve pop	12
Basket strainer	1
90° elbow	0.3
90° long elbow	0.15
T - flow through run	0.15
T - flow through branch	0.8
Gooseneck	3
90° bend	
r/d = 1*	0.5
r/d > 5	0.15
45° bend*	
r/d = 1	0.15

* r = bend radius; d = pipe diameter.

† Use velocity in smaller pipe for expansions and contractions.

(Table continued on next page.)

Table 5-2   Minor loss *k*-values (continued)

Component	k-values
r/d > 5	0.08
Mitre bends	
90°	1.2
60°	0.5
30°	0.14
Expansion[†]	
d/D = 0.75	0.18
d/D = 0.5	0.55
d/D = 0.25	0.88
Contraction[†]	
d/D = 0.25	0.43
d/D = 0.50	0.33
d/D = 0.75	0.18
Entrance	
Projecting	0.78
Flush	0.5
Slightly rounded	0.23
Well rounded	0.04
Exit	1

* r = bend radius; d = pipe diameter.
† Use velocity in smaller pipe for expansions and contractions.

Table 5-3   Minor loss through meters (continued)

Meter Type	Meter Size, *in.*	Peak Q, *gpm*	Loss at Peak Q, *psi*	*k*
Displacement	½	15	15	9.0
	½ × ¾	15	15	9.0
	⅝	20	15	5.1
	¾	30	15	4.7
	1	50	15	4.5
	1½	100	15	6.7
	2	160	15	8.3
Turbine (Class I)	¾	30	15	4.7
	1	50	15	5.3
	1½	100	15	6.7
	2	160	15	8.3
	3	350	15	8.8
	4	630	15	8.6
	6	1,300	15	10.2
Turbine (Class II)	1½	120	7	2.2
	2	190	7	2.7
	3	435	7	2.7
	4	750	7	2.8
	6	1,600	7	3.1
	8	2,800	7	3.2
	10	4,200	7	3.5

(Table continued on next page.)

Table 5-3   Minor loss through meters (continued)

Meter Type	Meter Size, *in.*	Peak Q, *gpm*	Loss at Peak Q, *psi*	*k*
	12	5,300	7	4.6
	16	7,800	7	6.7
	20	12,000	7	6.9
Fire service (Type II compound)	3	350	12	7.0
	4	700	12	5.5
	6	1,600	12	5.4
	8	2,800	12	5.5
	10	4,400	12	5.5
Fire service (Type III turbine with strainer)	3	350	11	6.4
	4	700	11	5.1
	6	1,600	11	4.9
	8	2,800	11	5.1
	10	4,400	11	5.0
Propeller (main line)	2	120	5	4.9
	3	300	5	4.0
	4	600	2	1.3
	5	900	1	0.7
	6	1,350	1	0.6
	8	1,800	0.5	0.6
	10	2,400	0.5	0.8
	12	3,375	0.5	0.8
	14	4,500	0.5	0.8
	16	5,700	0.5	0.9
	18	6,750	0.25	0.5
	20	8,250	0.25	0.5
	24	12,000	0.25	0.5
	30	18,000	0.25	0.6
	36	24,000	0.25	0.6
	42	40,000	0.1	0.2
	48	50,000	0.1	0.2
	54	55,000	0.1	0.2
	60	80,000	0.1	0.2
	66	95,000	0.1	0.2
	72	115,000	0.1	0.2
Multijet	5/8	20	15	5.1
	5/8 × 3/4	20	15	5.1
	3/4	30	15	4.7
	1	50	15	5.3
	1½	100	15	6.7
	2	160	15	8.3
Singlejet	5/8	20	15	5.1
	5/8 × 3/4	20	15	5.1
	3/4	30	15	4.7
	1	50	15	5.3
	1½	100	15	6.7
	2	160	15	8.3

(Table continued on next page.)

Table 5-3   Minor loss through meters (continued)

Meter Type	Meter Size, *in.*	Peak Q, *gpm*	Loss at Peak Q, *psi*	*k*
	3	320	15	10.5
	4	500	15	13.6
	6	1,000	15	17.2
Fluidic oscillator	½	15	15	9.0
	½ × ¾	15	15	9.0
	⅝	20	15	5.1
	⅝ × ¾	20	15	5.1
	¾	30	15	4.7
	1	50	15	5.3
	1½	100	15	6.7
	2	160	15	8.3
Residential fire sprinkler (meter only)	¾	30	10.1	3.1
	1	50	10.7	3.8
	1½	100	7.7	3.4
	2	160	7.7	4.3
Residential fire sprinkler (meter with strainer)	¾	30	14.5	4.5
	1	50	15.3	5.4
	1½	100	11	4.9
	2	160	11	6.1

Unlike k, which is dimensionless and independent of diameter, C_v has units and is a function of diameter. Manufacturers of valves usually provide a table giving the C_v for a valve as a function of diameter. When C_v is known at one diameter (C_{v1}) and it is desired to know it at a second diameter (C_{v2}), it can be approximated using the following equation 5-9:

$$C_{v2} = (C_{v1})\,(D_2/D_1)^2 \qquad \text{(Eq. 5-9)}$$

Substituting back into the equation for head loss, the head loss can be reasonably approximated at other diameters (D_2), given the head loss at a single diameter (D_1) using the following equation 5-10:

$$h = 2.31\,(Q/C_{v1})^2\,(D_1/D_2)^4 \qquad \text{(Eq. 5-10)}$$

For computer models, it may be necessary to enter a minor loss, k. The k value can be calculated from C_v at a given diameter using the following:

$$k = 885\,D^4/C_v^{\,2} \qquad \text{(Eq. 5-11)}$$

Minor loss versus Q curve. For some devices such as meters and backflow prevention assemblies, the head loss is given as a curve of head loss (or pressure drop) versus flow rate. For manual calculations, it is acceptable to simply look up the head loss from such a graph. For spreadsheet calculations, it may be necessary to determine an equation relating head loss and flow rate. The two types of curves are shown in Figure 5-1 and may be characterized as

- Those that pass through the origin, which is typical of meters and most valves.

- Those that have a discrete head loss before they open, which is typical of backflow prevention assemblies.

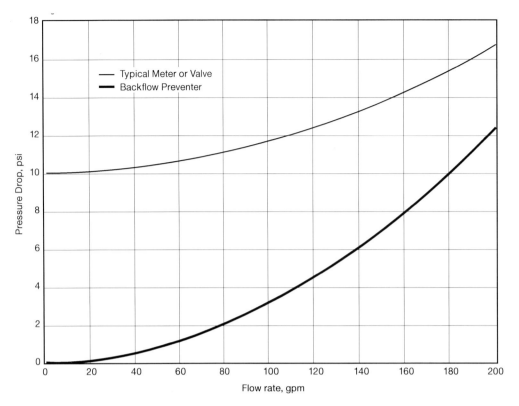

Figure 5-1   Head loss versus flow rate curves

For devices with head loss curves that pass through the origin, the head loss can be approximated as equation 5-12:

$$h = a\, Q^b \tag{Eq. 5-12}$$

Where:

a, b = regression coefficients

For most devices, b is on the order of 2. The values for a and b can be found by using a regression program or by picking two points from the curve (in the range of the expected flows), say (Q_1, h_1) and (Q_2, h_2), and calculating as follows:

$$b = \log (h_2 / h_1) / \log (Q_2 / Q_1)$$

$$a = h_1 / Q_1^{\,b}$$

One problem with determining values of a and b is that they are a function of diameter. An alternative approach is to calculate the minor loss, k, for the meter. This method is usually not as good a fit to the manufacturer's curve, but it is relatively independent of diameter for a given meter or valve model. The value of k can be determined by selecting a point near the design flow at the expected diameter and solving for k using equation 5-13:

$$k = 885\, pD^4 / Q^2 \tag{Eq. 5-13}$$

Where:

p = pressure drop, *psi*
Q = flow rate, *gpm*
D = diameter, *in.*

In the situation in which there is a discrete head loss before the valve opens (e.g., certain backflow prevention assemblies), the head loss can be given as equation 5-14:

$$h = h_{min} + aQ^b \qquad \text{(Eq. 5-14)}$$

Where:

h_{min} = head loss when $Q = 0$, *ft*
a, b = regression constants (differs from a and b of equation 5-12)

The values of a and b can be calculated using the following equations:

$$b = \log ([h_2 - h_{min}]/[h_1 - h_{min}]) / \log (Q_2 /Q_1) \qquad \text{(Eq. 5-15)}$$

$$a = (h_1 - h_{min})/Q^b \qquad \text{(Eq. 5-16)}$$

As was the case with valves, the curve of which passes through the origin, it is possible to model the loss using a minor loss, k. The modeling can be done by selecting a point from the curve at the design flow expected and calculating k as equation 5-17:

$$k = 885 \, (p - p_{min}) \, D^4/Q^2 \qquad \text{(Eq. 5-17)}$$

Where:

p_{min} = $h_{min}/2.31$, *psi*

Valves with a discrete pressure drop are handled differently in different pipe network hydraulic models. In some cases, they can be modeled as a negative pump curve; in others, they can be modeled as a discrete pressure drop in series with a minor loss; and in still others, they can be described directly to the model as a series of data points on a head loss versus flow curve. The k values for backflow prevention assemblies as given in Table 5-4 are based on the values given in the AWWA standards C510 and C511 and, as is the case with meters, values for actual assemblies are usually less.

Equivalent length. In some cases, an equivalent pipe length (L/D) is specified instead of a minor loss, k. The minor loss, k, can be determined from the Hazen–Williams equation as:

$$k = 194 \, C^{1.85}D^{0.167}V^{0.148} \, (L/D) \qquad \text{(Eq. 5-18)}$$

where C, D, and V refer to the properties of the equivalent pipe. For most cases, this can be simplified to equation 5-19:

$$k = 0.02 \, (L/D) \qquad \text{(Eq. 5-19)}$$

and the minor loss, k, can be used as previously described.

Table 5-4   Minor loss through backflow prevention assemblies

Type	Nominal Size, in.	Max Q, gpm	P open, psi	Max P psi	k
Reduced pressure	½	7.5	10	22	4.6
	¾	30	10	20	3.1
	1	50	10	18	2.8
	1¼	75	10	18	3.1
	1½	100	10	16	2.7
	2	160	10	16	3.3
	2½	225	10	16	4.1
	3	320	10	15	3.5
	4	500	10	14	3.6
	6	1,000	10	14	4.6
	8	1,600	10	14	5.7
	10	2,300	10	14	6.7
Double check valve	½	7.5	4	10	2.3
	¾	30	4	10	1.9
	1	50	4	10	2.1
	1¼	75	4	10	2.3
	1½	100	4	10	2.7
	2	160	4	10	3.3
	2½	225	4	10	4.1
	3	320	4	10	4.2
	4	500	4	10	5.4
	6	1,000	4	10	6.9
	8	1,600	4	10	8.5
	10	2,300	4	10	10.0

NOTE: k based on $885 \times (\text{max P} - \text{P open}) D^4/Q^2$.

Orifices. In most cases, it is not necessary to determine head loss through the actual orifice, nozzle, or sprinkler head. In some situations, however, it does become necessary. Most orifices can be given by an equation similar to the equation where C_v is previously defined. For orifices discharging to the atmosphere, the downstream pressure is atmospheric.

In some applications, sprinkler manufacturers describe the head loss through their sprinklers using a K value, which should not be confused with the minor loss, k. The k value is a carrying-capacity value like C_v. Solving for flow rate through a sprinkler can best be done using a hydraulic model (especially if more than one sprinkler is flowing at a time) (Walski 1995).

For details on sizing services for fire sprinkler systems, the reader should consult NFPA 13 (NFPA 2013a) for commercial and industrial buildings; NFPA 13R (NFPA 2013b) for residential occupancies up to four stories, and NFPA 13D (NFPA 2013c) for residential structures and manufactured buildings of three stories or smaller. Readers are also recommended to consult the *Water Purveyors Guide to Fire Sprinklers in Single Family Dwellings* (National Fire Sprinkler Association 2006), which gives information specific to water utilities in creating policies and requirements for water supply to sprinklered dwellings. This publication includes information on the applicable codes and standards, residential fire meters, backflow prevention, installation arrangements, hydraulic requirements, fees and charges, inspection, testing and maintenance, and options for rural water systems. Another good resource is the guide *Understanding Water Supply for Home Fire Sprinkler Systems* (Home Fire Sprinkler Coalition 2012), which features an informative video.

PERFORMING SIZING CALCULATIONS

The approach used to select and validate the service size depends on the complexity of the system and the form in which the data are presented. Approaches range from simple manual calculations based on consultation with tables to sophisticated computerized hydraulic models of the service line and piping.

For single-family residences, a ¾-in. service line with a ⅝-in. meter is typical. In general, the cost to install a larger service line when the building is being constructed is very small, whereas the cost to upsize later is significant. It is generally best to be conservative when sizing service lines. For example, assume the pressure in the main is 80 psi, and the customer only needs 30 psi. The service line can be sized for a pressure drop of 50 psi, but for only a slightly greater cost, the service line can be sized to provide a 10-psi drop and give the customer 70 psi. The decision is a trade-off between quality of service and cost. Utilities could eliminate many of their low-pressure complaints by conservatively sizing their service lines.

Using a standard pipe size for a residential customer (e.g., ¾ in. or 1 in.) may not be adequate if the pressures in the main are marginal, if the customer is located at a significantly higher elevation than the main, if the customer is set back far from the main, or if the customer has some large water uses (e.g., fire or irrigation sprinkler systems). Even for single-family residences, some hydraulic analysis may be necessary, notably homes requiring residential fire sprinklers.

All of the calculations start with the determination of the design flow, the available pressure, required pressure, length of the service line, and elevations of both the main and the customer's system. Flow and pressure requirements for residential fire sprinklers are provided in the NFPA 13D standard. Once the flow and pressure requirements are known, the engineer then selects the size of the piping, valves, and meters and calculates the head loss at the design flow rate or the flow rate that can be delivered using the available head. Pipe and fixture sizes are adjusted until the flow and head requirements are met without excessive cost.

In addition to sizing the service line to provide adequate pressure, the size should also be selected to prevent water hammer. Velocities greater than 10 ft/sec should be avoided, even if the service line can provide adequate pressure at these high velocities. The maximum recommended velocities for some materials may be substantially lower than 10 ft/sec. The pipe manufacturer should be consulted to obtain the recommended maximum velocity.

A schematic of head loss from the water main to the customer is shown in Figure 5-2. Design involves selecting a large-enough pipe and meter such that the drop in the hydraulic grade line is acceptable. The steps for determining the size of pipes, meters, and other fittings are shown in the flow chart in Figure 5-3.

At one extreme, the calculations can be performed by looking up the head loss through pipes and valves in tables as given in appendix B. This approach does not require the use of a computer but is the most cumbersome when performing iterative calculations trading off pipe size and cost. To simplify the repetitive calculations, a spreadsheet can be set up to perform the calculations. The challenge is to convert the graphs of head loss (or pressure drop) versus flow, for meters and backflow valves provided by manufacturers, into equations using the methods described earlier. Once the equations are derived, however, it is very easy to perform repeated calculations.

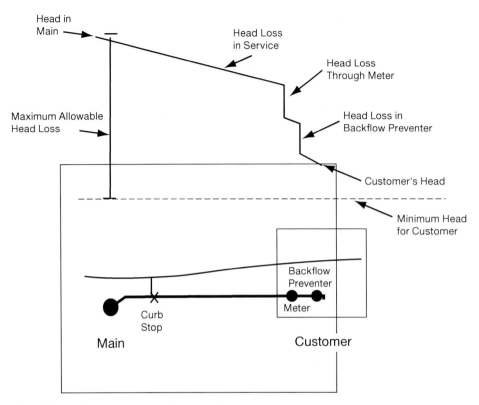

Figure 5-2   Head loss from water main to customer

When the service line is complicated with branches or if the designer wants to calculate the hydraulics of the system down to sprinkler heads and outlets, a hydraulic model is the ideal approach to sizing. In this case, the engineer must enter the coefficients for each device into the model.

While most engineers would initially feel that the manual approach is the easiest for a single calculation, spreadsheets and models are much easier should the customer come back with changes. For example, "Suppose we change the design flow to 120 gpm," or "We just found out we will need a minimum of 45 psi to make the equipment function." With a computerized calculation, repeating the calculation for these "what if " scenarios is very easy.

Each of these approaches (manual calculations, spreadsheet calculations, and hydraulic models) is illustrated in the following figures by calculating a recommendation for the same problem.

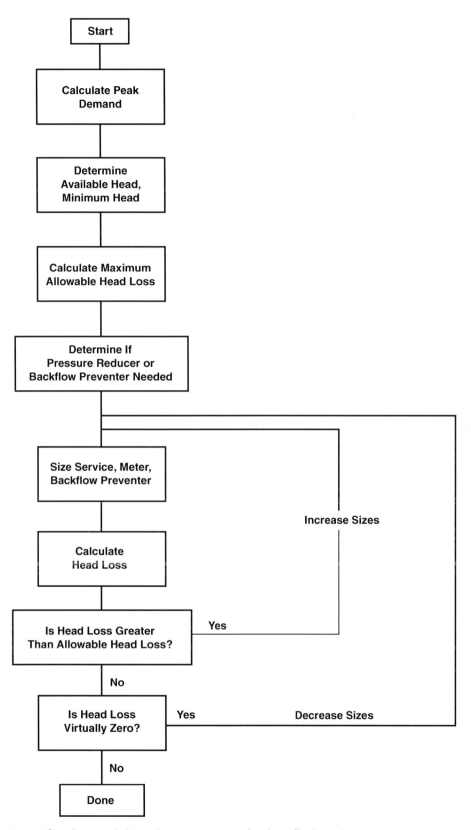

Figure 5-3   Steps for determining pipe, meter, and other fitting sizes

Example Sizing Problem

In this problem, there is a service line with the following characteristics:

Design flow rate	= 75 gpm
Service length	= 200 ft
Elevation of main	= 585.2 ft
Elevation of meter	= 598.1 ft
Design pressure in main	= 45 psi
Required pressure for customer	= 20 psi
Pipe material	= Type L copper tubing

There will be a compound meter and a RPBP assembly. The pressure drop versus head loss curves for these devices are shown in Figures 5-4 and 5-5. Losses through the corporation stopcock and curb stop can be considered negligible. Use a conservative value of C as 130.

$$\text{Available head loss} = 585.2 - 598.1 + 2.31\,(45 - 20) = 45 \text{ ft}$$

Manual, spreadsheet, and hydraulic model approaches to solving this problem are illustrated in the following sections.

Manual calculation. The manual approach is best suited for simple systems in which the range of choices in size is limited (e.g., typical domestic system with no sprinklers). In manual calculations, pressure drop in psi is sometimes used in place of head loss in feet. Convert the 45 ft available head to pressure drop in psi.

$$p = 45/2.31 = 19.5 \text{ psi allowable pressure drop}$$

Assume, initially, that a 2-in. nominal size pipe with a 2-in. meter and a 2-in. RPBP assembly will be used. The velocity in 2-in. copper tubing (actual ID = 1.985 in.) is 7.76 ft/sec using the tables in Appendix B. For manual calculations, the entrance loss into the service can be ignored. The pressure drop per 100 ft of piping is 5.8 psi. For 200 ft of line, this rate results in a pressure drop of 11.6 psi.

From Figure 5-4, the pressure drop in the meter is 1.5 psi. From Figure 5-5, the pressure drop through the RPBP assembly is 11.0 psi.

Summing the pressure drops gives the total pressure drop as:

$$p = 11.6 + 1.5 + 11.0 = 24.1 \text{ psi, which exceeds the allowable pressure drop}$$

The pipe, meter, and RPBP assembly need to be upsized and the calculations repeated until a satisfactory combination is found. Leaving the size of the RPBP assembly and meter the same and upsizing the pipe to 2½ in. will prove satisfactory in this instance. A larger pipe size may be desirable to provide better pressure and to provide a margin for error.

Spreadsheet calculation. It takes somewhat longer to initially set up a spreadsheet, but repeat calculations are very easy. For the same example addressed by the manual calculation, the head loss equations used are summarized below:

Pipe loss:
Using Eq. 5-3:

$$h = 10.4\,(200)\,(75/130)^{1.85}\,D^{-4.87} = 752\,D^{-4.87}$$

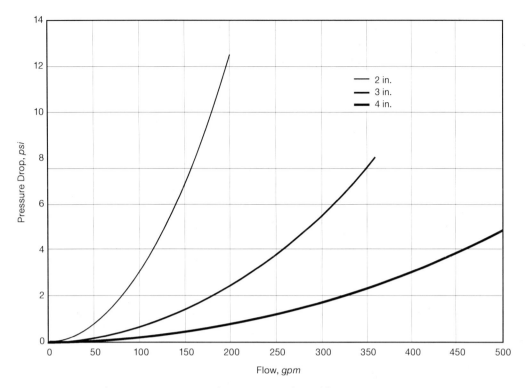

Figure 5-4   Compound-meter pressure drop versus head loss curves

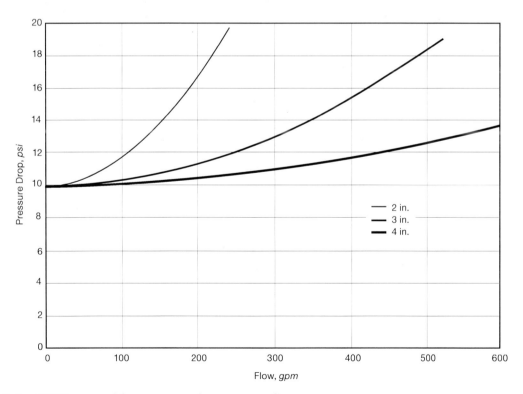

Figure 5-5   RPBP assembly pressure drop versus flow curves

Entrance loss:
Using Eq. 5-6:

$$h = 0.5 \ (75^2)/(383 \ D^4)$$

Meter loss: The meter in question has a pressure drop of 8 psi at 160 gpm in the 2-in. size. Therefore, from Eq. 5-13:

$$k = 885(8)2^4/(160^2) = 4.42$$

Head loss: The head loss can be calculated using Eq. 5-6 as:

$$h = 4.42 \ (75^2)/(383 \ D^4) = 64.9/D^4$$

Backflow prevention assembly: The backflow-prevention assembly has a value for h_{min} of 10 psi or 23.1 ft and the k value can be calculated using 14-psi drop in the 2 in. at 160 gpm as:

$$k = 885 \ (p - p_{min}) \ D^4/Q^2 = 2.2$$

For the 2-in. assembly, this gives:

$$h = 23.1 + 2.2 \ (75^2)/(383 \ D^4)$$

The results of the spreadsheet calculation are shown in Table 5-5, and they indicate that a 2.5-in. diameter service line and meter would be acceptable, as shown in variation 2. Because this is an uncommon size, a 3-in. diameter is selected. Note that variations 3 through 6 would also be viable design alternatives.

Table 5-5   Service-line sizing calculation spreadsheet (L = 200 ft, Q = 75 gpm)

Variables	Variation 1	Variation 2	Variation 3	Variation 4	Variation 5	Variation 6
D, in nominal pipe	2	2.5	3	2.5	3	3.5
D, in meter	2	2.5	3	2	3	2
D, in RPBP	2	2.5	3	2	2.5	2.5
D, in actual pipe	1.985	2.465	2.945	2.465	2.465	3.425
Available head, *ft*	44.8	44.8	44.8	44.8	44.8	44.8
Calculated parameters						
Pipe loss, *ft*	26.7	9.3	3.9	9.3	9.3	1.9
Entrance loss, *ft*	0.5	0.2	0.1	0.2	0.1	0.0
Meter loss, *ft*	4.1	1.7	0.8	4.1	0.8	4.1
RPBP, loss	25.3	24.0	23.5	25.3	24.0	24.0
Total loss, *ft*	56.5	35.1	28.3	38.8	34.2	30.0
Available loss, *ft*	−11.7	9.7	16.5	6.0	10.6	14.8
Velocity, *ft/sec*	15.5	12.5	10.4	12.5	12.5	9.0

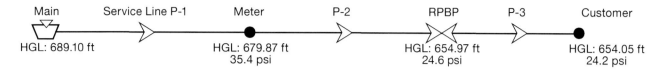

Key:
HGL = hydraulic gradient line
P1 = service line from the main to the meter
P2 = line from the meter to the RPBP
P3 = line from the RPBP to customer
RPBP = reduced-pressure backflow prevention assembly

Figure 5-6   Hydraulic model used to determine head loss: 75 gpm, 2.5-in. meter scenario

Hydraulic model. The hydraulic model used to determine the head loss is shown in Figure 5-6. With a model, the service line can be represented as a single pipe with several minor losses corresponding to the service line or several pipes in series. For example, the service line P1 from the main to the upstream side of the meter, the line P2 from the meter to the backflow prevention assembly, and the line P3 downstream from the backflow prevention assembly to the point where the customer pressure are measured. In the same example addressed by the manual and spreadsheet calculations, the service line is divided into 198 ft of pipe, a 1-ft pipe corresponds to the head loss of the meter, another 1-ft pipe corresponds to the head loss in the backflow prevention assembly, and a pressure breaker valve simulates the discrete pressure drop before the RPBP will open. For this sample problem, the backflow prevention assembly is represented as a pressure breaker valve with a loss of 23.1 ft in series with a minor loss, *k*, of 2.2 as previously calculated.

With a model, more information can be obtained than from a manual calculation, such as the pressure at any point along the line, the velocity in each pipe, and the hydraulic grade line (head) at any point along the line. Once a model is set up, the "what if " calculations are easy to perform.

Selection. For the sample problem addressed in the preceding discussion, several alternative combinations of pipe and valve sizes will provide adequate flow capacity for the head available. The final decision will be based on the economics of the situation, the accuracy range of the meter, and the amount of safety factor the engineer would like to include.

REFERENCES
American Society of Civil Engineers (ASCE). 1992. *Pressure Pipeline Design for Water and Wastewater.* Committee on Pipeline Planning. New York: ASCE.

American Water Works Association (AWWA). ANSI/AWWA Standard C510. Double Check Valve Backflow-Prevention Assembly. Denver, Colo.: AWWA.

AWWA. ANSI/AWWA Standard C511. Reduced Pressure Principle Backflow-Prevention Assembly. Denver, Colo.: AWWA.

AWWA. ANSI/AWWA Standard C700. Cold Water Meters—Displacement Type, Bronze Main Case. Denver, Colo.: AWWA.

AWWA. ANSI/AWWA Standard C701. Cold Water Meters—Turbine Type, for Customer Service. Denver, Colo.: AWWA.

AWWA. ANSI/AWWA Standard C702. Cold Water Meters—Compound Type. Denver, Colo.: AWWA.

AWWA. ANSI/AWWA Standard C703. Cold Water Meters—Fire Service Type. Denver, Colo.: AWWA.

AWWA. ANSI/AWWA Standard C704. Propeller-Type Meters for Waterworks Applications. Denver, Colo.: AWWA.

AWWA. ANSI/AWWA Standard C708. Cold Water Meters—Multijet Type. Denver, Colo.: AWWA.

AWWA ANSI/AWWA Standard C710. Cold Water Meters—Displacement Type, Plastic Main Case. Denver, Colo.: AWWA.

AWWA ANSI/AWWA Standard C712. Cold Water Meters—Singlejet Type. Denver, Colo.: AWWA.

AWWA. ANSI/AWWA Standard C713. Cold Water Meters—Fluidic Oscillator Type. Denver Colo.: AWWA.

AWWA. ANSI/AWWA Standard C714. Cold Water Meters for Residential Fire Sprinkler Systems in One- and Two-Family Dwellings and Manufactured Homes. Denver Colo.: AWWA.

AWWA. ANSI/AWWA Standard C750. Transit-Time Flowmeters in Full Closed Conduits. Denver, CO: AWWA.

AWWA. ANSI/AWWA Standard C800. Underground Service Line Valves and Fittings. Denver, Colo.: AWWA.

AWWA. 2004. Manual M14, *Recommended Practice for Backflow Prevention and Cross-Connection Control.* Denver, Colo.: AWWA.

Brock, P.D. 1993. *Fire Protection Hydraulics and Water Supply Analysis.* Fire Protection Publications. Stillwater, Okla.: Oklahoma State University.

Crane Co. 1969. *Flow of Fluids through Valves, Fittings, and Pipe.* Technical Paper 410. Stamford, Conn.: Crane.

Home Fire Sprinkler Coalition (HFSC). 2012. Understanding Water Supply for Home Fire Sprinkler Systems. Frankfort, IL: HFSC.

Hydraulic Institute. 1978. *Engineering Data Book.* Cleveland, Ohio: Hydraulic Institute.

National Fire Protection Association (NFPA). 2013a. NFPA 13, Installation of Sprinkler Systems. Quincy, Mass.: NFPA.

NFPA. 2013b. NFPA 13R, Installation of Sprinkler Systems in Low-Rise Residential Occupancies Quincy, Mass.: NFPA.

NFPA. 2013c. NFPA 13D, Sprinkler Systems in One- and Two-Family Dwellings and Manufactured Homes. Quincy, Mass.: NFPA.

National Fire Sprinkler Association (NFSA). 2006. Water Purveyors Guide to Fire Sprinklers in Single Family Dwellings. Patterson, NY: NFSA.

Walski, T.M. 1984. *Analysis of Water Distribution Systems.* New York: Van Nostrand-Reinhold.

Walski, T.M. 1994. An Approach for Handling Sprinklers, Hydrants, and Orifices in Water Distribution Models. Presented at AWWA ACE Convention, Anaheim, Calif.

Walski, T.M., and R.E. Clyne. 1996. Sizing Residential Service Lines. *Jour. AWWA* 11(10):70.

Chapter **6**

Sizing and Type Selection for the Customer's Meter

INTRODUCTION

The water meter is a changeable component of the customer's water system. Unlike the service line and water tap, which when incorrectly sized will generally require expensive excavation and retapping, water meters can usually be changed less expensively. The purpose of this chapter is to present guidelines on meter selection based on actual or likely demands. Undersizing the meter can cause pressure-related problems and can also result in lost revenue at high-end flows, and oversizing the meter can result in reduced revenue at low-end flows and inaccurate meter recordings.

REVENUE IMPLICATIONS

The sizing of the meters and services can have significant impacts on a utility's revenue. As the flow drops below the recommended flow range for a meter, the meter will under-register. Oversized meters can result in lost revenue because of inaccurate registration at low flow. From the standpoint of registration accuracy and revenue, water meters should not be sized conservatively. In addition to charging for water consumed, many water utilities have a charge based on tap (or service line) size or meter size, either every billing period or at the time of installation (e.g., tapping fee or capital recovery fee). Sizing decisions may, therefore, impact revenue through fixed charges based on meter size.

The recurring fixed charge is typically billed for a variety of routine services, such as customer meter reading, billing, and, perhaps, separate services, such as stormwater management. A number of water utilities have begun to charge for stormwater services as a distinct land parcel-based component on the water bill, thus lowering the fixed charge based on service line or meter size. The engineer should stay abreast of changes in the customer billing rate structure that are based on service line or meter size and understand the impacts that such changes might exert in meter-sizing decisions.

To size a water meter appropriately, the engineer needs to understand the utility's design criteria and determine the demand flow range of the customer's system. For existing services, empirical demand data may be the best source of information to ensure that the meter will meet actual needs. For new services, estimated demand must be calculated from other data. Chapters 3 and 4 provide two methods for estimating design flows. The objective is to ensure that the meter is of sufficient size to properly handle the likely demands as estimated by the engineer.

The engineer needs to understand all aspects of the customer's demands. Relevant demand information may be obtained by having the customer complete a form that describes the anticipated nature of the flow (e.g., steady always, steady flow during working day, high peaks when filling tanks, high peaks during irrigation, etc.), peak demand, flow range, inside or outside meter setting, and, for utilities that require metering of fire sprinkler systems, data regarding fire-service demands. Sprinkler and fire-service demands are especially important considerations, because they have a significant impact on meter type and size but do not appear on typical demand profiles based strictly on normal daily or weekly usage. This information will assist the engineer in determining the size and type of meter (i.e., positive displacement, multijet, singlejet, static, compound, or turbine) that will most accurately register water demands and meet the customer's needs. Note that water usage patterns at an existing metered site may change drastically over time. For example, older factory sites may be repurposed with conversions to apartments, retail, or light commercial applications. When water use changes, the water meter size or type may also need to be changed.

SYSTEM COMPONENTS POLICY REVIEW

After estimating the customer's peak demand and demand flow range as described in chapters 3 and 4, the next step is to collect data regarding the system components. The following field information may be required:

- Flow tests of the water main that serves the area, if available

- Pressure in the service provider's main during the customer's peak demand periods, if available

- Elevation differential of city main and customer's indoor piping

- Length of service pipe necessary to extend from the main to the meter

- The proposed size of pipe used by the customer from the meter to the building

- Effective pipe distance for the service line's fittings and valves

- Utility's engineering standards for service line, appurtenances, and meter installation

- Fire-line meter requirements

Information regarding the system flow capability, pressure, and depth and location of the water main, along with fire-line meter requirements, may be available from the utility. Elevation differential, length and size of service pipe, and fitting and valve specifications are information that the engineer will need to collect. After obtaining this information, the engineer should proceed with obtaining information about the utility's engineering standards and policies so that the service line and meter are installed according to the utility's specifications. Examples of questions the engineer may want to ask regarding the utility's standards and policies in order to determine the proper meter size include the following:

- Does the utility require the meter to be located at the property line?
- Does the utility allow the tapping of the fire line?
- Do the service line and meter need to be the same size?
- What are the utility's required service line and meter-setting design requirements?
- Does the utility require the fire-sprinkler system to be metered?
- What are the service line specifications to and from the meter?
- Are there maximum head loss or velocity requirements?

WATER METER SELECTION

Water meters are comparatively easy to replace; accordingly, if a meter is not properly sized, the expense of replacement is generally not cost prohibitive if sufficient space is available in the meter pit, vault, or the meter room inside a building.

The engineer should refer to each water meter manufacturer's specifications to determine if the meter selected to serve the customer can (1) accurately record the predicted maximum flow for short periods of time without damage or without above-normal wear occurring to the meter and (2) accurately record the anticipated range of flows. AWWA Manual M6 has information for cold-water meters on flow range capabilities and maximum pressure losses that can be used by the engineer. As new meter designs are developed that can operate accurately at different ranges of flow, however, the engineer should check with the utility to determine if such new meters are in accordance with the utility's requirements.

The engineer should use utility-approved meter manufacturers' specifications whenever possible to determine pressure loss, range of accuracy, and capacity. Table 6-1 provides minimum, normal, and maximum flow-range values for water meters based on AWWA water meter standards. These standards should be used as a guideline when meter manufacturers' data are not readily available. The engineer must be aware that there are several types of meters, and that they have different capacities and ranges of accuracies. This table is only a guide. (See AWWA Standards for meters: C700, C701, C702, C703, C704, C708, C710, C712, C713, C714, and C750)

A meter's normal flow range is the range within which meter performance is optimal. Excessive flow above the high normal-rate will cause excessive wear.

The engineer should know the distribution of flow rates when sizing the meter for a customer. For example, if 99.9 percent of a customer's flow is below 30 gpm, but the customer has a brief spike once a week of 40 gpm, the meter should be sized to accurately collect the 99.9 percent of the flow, provided the head loss during the spike is acceptable and the meter can survive this surge flow. Most meters can handle brief peak demands and still accurately record low volumes of water, so it is not necessary to ignore 99.9 percent of the volume simply to keep the instantaneous peak demand within the meter's specified flow range. The distribution of flow rates is also important in determining what type of meter is preferred for larger services.

Table 6-1   AWWA meter standards

Meter	Minimum Flow Rate, gpm	Low-Normal Flow Rate, gpm	Change-over Range (Compound Meters)	High-Normal Flow Rate, gpm	Maximum Flow Rate gpm	Head Loss at Maximum Flow, psi
Positive displacement						
½ in.	0.25	1	N/A	7.5	15	15
⅝ in.	0.25	1		10	20	15
¾ in.	0.50	2		15	30	15
1 in.	0.75	3		25	50	15
1½ in.	1.50	5		50	100	15
2 in.	2.00	8		80	160	15
Multijet						
⅝ in.	0.25	1	N/A	10	20	15
¾ in.	0.50	2		15	30	15
1 in.	0.75	3		25	50	15
1½ in.	1.50	5		50	100	15
2 in.	2.00	8		80	160	15
Turbine class II						
1½ in.	N/A	4	N/A	90	120	7
2 in.		4		160	190	7
3 in.		8		350	435	7
4 in.		15		650	750	7
6 in.		30		1,400	1,600	7
8 in.		50		2,400	2,800	7
10 in.		75		3,500	4,200	7
12 in.		120		4,400	5,300	7
16 in.		200		6,500	7,800	7
20 in.		300		10,000	12,000	7
Compound class II						
2 in.	0.25	1	13	80	160	15
3 in.	0.50	2	15	175	350	15
4 in.	0.75	3	18	300	600	15
6 in.	1.50	5	20	675	1,350	15
8 in.	2.00	16	35	900	1,600	15
Fire service, type II—compound						
3 in	* see note	2	30	250	350	12
4 in.		4	40	400	700	12
6 in.		5	90	900	1,600	12
8 in.		8	150	1,600	2,800	12
10 in.		8	200	2,200	4,400	12

Source: Data are drawn from AWWA Standards C700, C701, C702, C703, C704, C708, C710, C712, C713, and C714, latest revision.

N/A = not applicable.

* Minimum flow rate is per the applicable AWWA standard for the bypass meter employed.

(Table continued on next page.)

Table 6-1   AWWA meter standards (continued)

Meter	Minimum Flow Rate, gpm	Low-Normal Flow Rate, gpm	Change-over Range (Compound Meters)	High-Normal Flow Rate, gpm	Maximum Flow Rate gpm	Head Loss at Maximum Flow, psi
Fire service, type III—turbine						
3 in.	4	5	N/A	250	350	11
4 in.	10	15		400	700	11
6 in.	20	30		900	1,600	11
8 in.	30	35		1,600	2,800	11
10 in.	35	55		2,500	4,400	11
Propeller (main line)						
2 in.	N/A	45	N/A	100	120	5
3 in.		80		250	300	5
4 in.		85		500	600	2
6 in.		160		1,200	1,350	1
8 in.		190		1,500	1,800	0.5
10 in.		260		2,000	2,400	0.5
12 in.		275		2,800	3,375	0.5
14 in.		350		3,750	4,500	0.5
16 in.		450		4,750	5,700	0.5
18 in.		550		5,625	6,750	0.25
20 in.		650		6,875	8,250	0.25
24 in.		1,000		10,000	12,000	0.25
30 in.		1,600		15,000	18,000	0.25
36 in.		2,400		20,000	24,000	0.25
42 in.		2,800		28,000	40,000	0.1
48 in.		3,500		35,000	50,000	0.1
54 in.		5,000		45,000	55,000	0.1
60 in.		6,000		60,000	80,000	0.1
66 in.		7,500		75,000	95,000	0.1
72 in.		9,000		90,000	115,000	0.1
Fluidic oscillator						
½ in.	0.25	1	N/A	7.5	15	15
⅝ in.	0.25	1		10	20	15
¾ in.	0.50	2		15	30	15
1 in.	0.75	3		25	50	15
1½ in.	1.50	5		50	100	15
2 in.	2.00	8		80	160	15
Singlejet						
⅝ in.	0.25	1	N/A	10	20	15
¾ in.	0.50	2		15	30	15
1 in.	0.75	3		20	40	15
1½ in.	0.50	1.5	N/A	50	100	15

Source: Data are drawn from AWWA Standards C700, C701, C702, C703, C704, C708, C710, C712, C713, and C714, latest revision.

N/A = not applicable.

* Minimum flow rate is per the applicable AWWA standard for the bypass meter employed.

(Table continued on next page.)

Table 6-1   AWWA meter standards (continued)

Meter	Minimum Flow Rate, gpm	Low-Normal Flow Rate, gpm	Change-over Range (Compound Meters)	High-Normal Flow Rate, gpm	Maximum Flow Rate gpm	Head Loss at Maximum Flow, psi
2 in.	0.50	2.0		80	160	15
3 in.	0.50	2.5		160	320	15
4 in.	0.75	3.0		250	500	15
6 in	1.50	4.0		500	1,000	15
Residential Fire Sprinkler						
¾ in.	0.5	2	N/A	15	30	10.1
1 in.	0.75	2		25	50	10.7
1½ in.	1.5	3		50	100	7.7
2 in.	2.0	4		80	160	7.7
Residential Fire Sprinkler w/ strainer						
¾ in.	0.5	2	N/A	15	30	14.5
1 in.	0.75	2		25	50	15.3
1½ in.	1.5	3		50	100	11
2 in.	2.0	4		80	160	11

Source: Data are drawn from AWWA Standards C700, C701, C702, C703, C704, C708, C710, C712, C713, and C714, latest revision.

N/A = not applicable.

* Minimum flow rate is per the applicable AWWA standard for the bypass meter employed.

Table 6-2   Typical uses for each type of meter classification

Meter Type	Typical Use
Positive displacement, fluidic oscillator, multijet, singlejet, static, turbine, electromagnetic, or ultrasonic	Single-family residential, apartment buildings with fewer than 100 units; small businesses (e.g., filling stations, restaurants, small hotels, motels, small office buildings, retail stores, etc.); schools and other public buildings without large irrigation demands
Turbine, singlejets, static, electromagnetic or ultrasonic	Large hotels, factories, hospitals, irrigation, large office buildings, pump discharge, laundries, nursing homes
Compound, singlejets, turbine, multijet, static, electromagnetic or ultrasonic	Schools (with irrigation), apartment buildings with more than 100 units, dormitories, assisted living centers, retail shopping centers
Residential fire meters	One- and two-family dwellings and manufactured homes (NFPA 13D applications)
Fire-line meters	Fire service (for various NFPA 13 and NFPA 13R applications)
Differential pressure (venturi, flow tube), electromagnetic or ultrasonic meters	Pump discharge, wholesale water purchasers, research applications, subsystem metering

Although the selection of the type and size of meter should be based primarily on the range of flow and peak demand, pressure loss through the meter should also be a consideration. Oversizing a meter to reduce pressure loss can result in unregistered water usage during low-flow periods, which increases nonrevenue water. Undersizing may cause increased maintenance costs as well as poor service to the customer.

If a meter is being sized for the first phase of a larger project, the meter could be sized for the initial phase with provision for installation of a larger meter in the future when expansion occurs. Similarly, if the engineer anticipates a greater demand by the customer at some point in the future, provision should be made to enable the installation of a larger meter. Again, the meter could be installed for current needs but with a meter box and connections that are adequate to meet anticipated future requirements.

Positive displacement meters are widely used because they accurately register low flows. Multijet, smaller singlejet, fluidic oscillator, and smaller vertical-shaft turbine meters have been used in some applications similar to those that employ positive displacement meters. Traditionally, turbine and propeller meters have been used when water usage is characterized by higher demands with few or no low flows because these meters may not register low flows as accurately as other meters. Compound meters are a combination of a smaller bypass meter and a larger (main-line) turbine-type meter. They register accurately across the largest range of flow rates. However, compound meters have higher wear and maintenance requirements and should be carefully selected to provide economical service. Singlejet designs, ultrasonic, electromagnetic, and newer turbine meter designs may be able to extend low-flow performance to levels nearing those of compound meters or even better. In order to maintain accurate readings, meters should be maintained on a regular basis and replaced as necessary.

Fire-line-meters for NFPA 13 and NFPA 13R sprinkler systems have historically been proportional meters. Fire insurance companies also recognize turbine meters and turbine meters with a check-valve bypass meter configuration that are equipped with UL or FM approved strainers. For residential applications, Underwriters Laboratories has issued residential fire-service listings for various metering technologies from several manufacturers (although NFPA 13D does not require a UL-listed product).

The selection of the type of meter is discussed further in AWWA Manual M6 (2012). Table 6-2 shows typical uses for the various types of meters.

All 3-in. and larger meter customers, such as hospitals, schools, and factories with processes requiring uninterrupted water service, should have bypasses installed around the meter so that meter test and repair activities can be performed at scheduled intervals without inconvenience to either the customer or the utility. The bypass should be valved and locked appropriately.

Additionally, plate strainers should be installed in front of turbine and compound meters. In some cases, these strainers are an integral part of the meter housing. The engineer should account for the head loss in the calculations.

While not yet addressed in AWWA meter standards, floating ball, electromagnetic, and ultrasonic metering technologies are now being extended into revenue billing applications at the retail level.

An example of a software program that uses demand profile data to determine appropriate meter sizing is provided in appendix A.

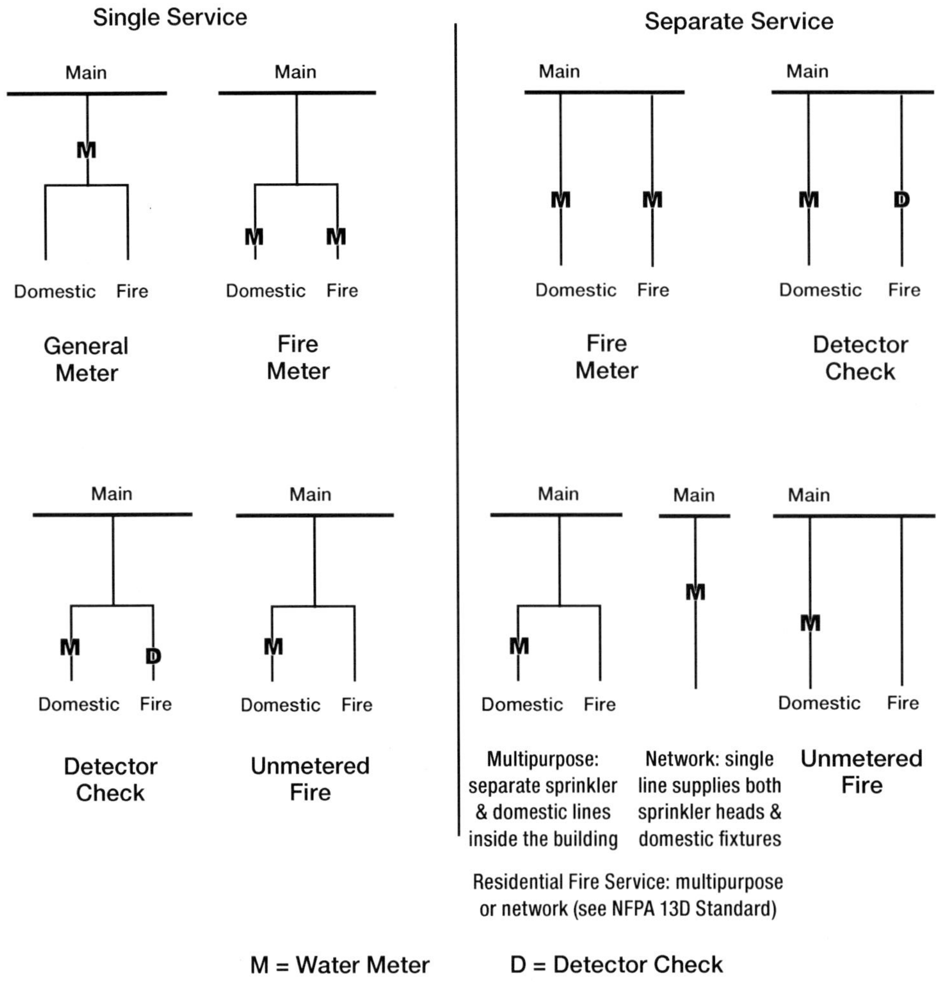

Figure 6-1   Some common arrangements for service lines and meters

METER ARRANGEMENTS FOR FIRE SERVICES

One of the key decisions in sizing service lines and meters is the arrangement of service lines and meters. Some utilities use a single tap for both fire and domestic use (including commercial/industrial), but other utilities use separate taps for domestic and fire use. In addition, some utilities meter fire use, some use a detector check-type meter, and others do not meter fire flows at all. Some of the most common arrangements for service lines and meters are shown in Figure 6-1.

The decision as to which service line and meter arrangement to use is a policy decision of the utility. Metering all fire flow (either with a separate meter or a general meter) maximizes water accountability. Use of a general meter requires a multi-register meter in some commercial/industrial applications, but a separate fire line makes it possible to function with a single, fire-type turbine meter on the fire line in these same applications. In some utilities, a policy exists to provide fire flow at no cost (or a flat fee) and fire flow need not be metered. In those cases, the utility may still want to use a detector check to minimize the likelihood of water theft from the fire line and to be able to identify the existence of leakage in the fire line.

SUMMARY

The meter should be correctly sized to handle and record the expected range of flow rates. Utility administrative policies should encourage good engineering. Too large a meter may result in unregistered water use at low flows, and too small a meter may result in pressure and maintenance problems. In all cases, the meter should be accurately sized to meet the customer's actual or projected demands and the utility's engineering criteria. AWWA meter standards and meter manufacturer specifications are the recommended guidelines for determining the correct meter type and size once anticipated or actual demand characteristics have been defined using either flow recorders or manual fixture-value calculations.

REFERENCES

American Water Works Association (AWWA). ANSI/AWWA Standard C700. Cold-Water Meters—Displacement Type, Bronze Main Case. Denver, Colo.: AWWA.

AWWA. ANSI/AWWA Standard C701. Cold-Water Meters—Turbine Type, for Customer Service. Denver, Colo.: AWWA.

AWWA. ANSI/AWWA Standard C702. Cold-Water Meters—Compound Type. Denver, Colo.: AWWA.

AWWA. ANSI/AWWA Standard C703. Cold-Water Meters—Fire-Service Type. Denver, Colo.: AWWA.

AWWA. ANSI/AWWA Standard C704. Propeller-Type Meters for Waterworks Applications. Denver, Colo.: AWWA.

AWWA. ANSI/AWWA Standard C706. Direct-Reading, Remote-Registration Systems for Cold-Water Meters. Denver, Colo.: AWWA.

AWWA. ANSI/AWWA Standard C707. Encoder-Type Remote-Registration Systems for Cold-Water Meters. Denver, Colo.: AWWA.

AWWA. ANSI/AWWA Standard C708. Cold-Water Meters—Multijet Type. Denver, Colo.: AWWA.

AWWA. ANSI/AWWA Standard C710. Cold-Water Meters—Displacement Type, Plastic Main Case. Denver, Colo.: AWWA.

AWWA. ANSI/AWWA Standard C712. Cold-Water Meters—Singlejet Type. Denver, Colo.: AWWA.

AWWA. ANSI/AWWA Standard C713. Cold-Water Meters—Fluidic Oscillator Type. Denver, Colo.: AWWA.

AWWA. ANSI/AWWA Standard C714. Cold-Water Meters for Residential Fire Sprinkler Systems in One- and Two-Family Dwellings and Manufactured Homes. Denver, Colo.: AWWA.

AWWA. ANSI/AWWA Standard C750. Transit-Time Flowmeters in Full Closed Conduits. Denver, Colo.: AWWA.

AWWA. Manual M6. *Water Meters—Selection, Installation, Testing, and Maintenance.* Denver, Colo.: AWWA.

This page intentionally blank.

Appendix A

Software to Size a Meter

INTRODUCTION

The most accurate way to size a meter is to record detailed demand data for a particular customer or a similar customer during a period of typical usage and then to calculate the accounted-for water percentage, percentage of flow in a meter's normal range, and the head loss at the maximum recorded flow rate for each possible meter type and size option. Because such calculations involve a great many variables and are too time consuming to do efficiently by hand, the engineer should take advantage of spreadsheet or specialized meter sizing software to perform the calculations. This appendix illustrates how demand profile data and meter performance characteristics can be combined in meter sizing software to aid in meter selection.

The following is an overview of how meter-sizing software can use demand data in conjunction with meter performance specifications and utility-specific meter and financial information to perform the calculations on which proper meter sizing decisions are based. Once utility-specific information has been entered, the software can automatically estimate the projected percentage of accounted-for water and the annual revenue increase or decrease associated with each meter type and size option. It can also calculate the percentage of flow in each meter option's normal flow range, the number of months it would take for a meter changeout to pay for itself, and the head loss at maximum recorded flow for each meter option. The software accomplishes this by distributing high-resolution demand data collected at a meter site into software-defined flow ranges for each meter type and size option.

SUMMARY OF SOFTWARE OPERATION

Before beginning, the user should confirm or change the software defaults and enter utility-specific default information. Some software uses AWWA meter flow ranges and accuracy factors for positive displacement, multijet, turbine, and compound meters as found in AWWA water meter standards. The software should enable the user to edit these values if appropriate. Once the default values have been entered, the user imports a demand profile made using a flow recorder (i.e., a profile that provides flow rate through the meter versus time on some small interval such as 10 sec). The data can be entered manually; however, much of the advantage of using the software comes from its capacity to base its calculations on high-resolution rate information gathered over a period of time. If desired, a seasonal adjustment could be performed by entering the billing records for the previous year, and the flow rates would be scaled up or down proportionately.

At this point, sufficient data has been entered to perform calculations. The software can rank meters based on accounted-for water and determine the amount of flow in each meter's normal range, the head loss at the maximum recorded flow rate, and the financial impact of each meter alternative. A graphic analysis feature can enable a user to view each meter's maximum, minimum, high-normal, and low-normal flow rates superimposed over the actual demand profile for a given installation.

SETUP

Current meter sizing software is designed around AWWA meter performance standards and comes with defaults that permit a meter sizing analysis to be performed without altering the default AWWA parameters (Figure A-1). Nevertheless, the defaults and software assumptions must be reviewed before making any sizing decisions based on software results. Certain defaults, such as the rates of flow applicable to compound meter changeover ranges, do not have AWWA standard values; accordingly, software should use reasonable default values based on consultation with industry professionals.

The software should enable all assumptions to be tailored to meet the unique requirements and characteristics of any utility. Many utilities have their own standards of meter performance, which represent local conditions or tests, and each utility has a unique financial structure. The minimum setup requirements for performing a financial analysis are (a) the retail cost of water (and related wastewater rates, if applicable); (b) fixed charges for each meter type and size; (c) changeout costs for each meter type and size (labor and materials); and (d) the average monthly maintenance charge for each meter type and size. For example, compound meters typically have higher maintenance costs than turbines, and this should be reflected in the analysis.

A software program could include information about each meter type and size's accuracy in various flow ranges. AWWA standards can be used as defaults for these values although information provided by manufacturers may be more appropriate. These values are: the maximum and minimum flow rates; the flow rates defining the normal flow range; the changeover flow range (for compound meters); the head loss at the maximum flow rate; and accounted-for water accuracy ratings for each applicable flow range.

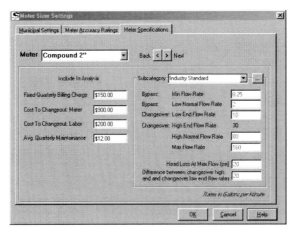

Figure A-1   Meter specifications screen (sample from *MeterSizer*®)

Courtesy of F.S. Brainard and Co.

Because meters do not stop registering flow for rates above and below AWWA standard accuracy ranges, software should also make assumptions for performance in these ranges. Default values for these assumptions are developed in consultation with industry professionals. While a user may change these assumptions by adding other categories with their own values, the software default should be used unless the user has a good basis for using alternate values.

SIZING A METER

Once all of the meter performance and utility financial information has been entered/confirmed, sizing a meter is a seven-step procedure.

1. Site Survey

If possible, a questionnaire should be completed to ensure that the period chosen for recording the consumption profile is representative of the user's typical usage patterns. If it is not, the field test should be rescheduled for a more appropriate time period. Peak flow events should also be captured. If such events are seasonal, the customer should be profiled during normal demand and peak demand periods. For example, food processing plants work all year but are busiest during harvest time. Usage data from a customer's billing history can also be used to verify that the amount of water used during the data-storage period is representative. A questionnaire can also be used to identify the potential sources of peak and minimum flows.

2. Consumption Profile

A consumption profile should be recorded using a data logger/recording device and then imported into the software. A minimum of 24 hr is recommended for residential applications. Longer periods are recommended for commercial/industrial accounts because significant uses of water may only occur on certain days of the week.

3. Import/Enter Customer Information

Customer information and the actual demand data is imported into the software, or entered directly by typing into screen fields (Figure A-2).

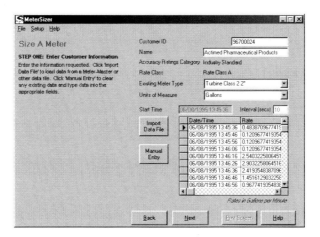

Figure A-2   Customer information screen (sample from *MeterSizer®*)

Courtesy of F.S. Brainard and Co.

4. Seasonal Adjustment

To adjust data for seasonal variations in water use, an option can be provided on another screen to enter the customer's most recent annual billing history. This data enables software to consider the impact of changes in seasonal consumption patterns in the meter sizing decision if it is reasonable to assume that the pattern in different seasons is consistent, with only the quantity of water used varying. If the average daily usage during the maximum-usage billing period is 20 percent higher than during the data-recording period, all rate values could be increased 20 percent, for example.

5. Initial Results

As an example of displaying results, *MeterSizer*® automatically shows the accounted-for and financial impacts associated with the best meter option for the application (Figure A-3). Left/right arrows and a scroll bar allow the user to view results for all meter options. Meters are ranked from best to worst based on their percentage of accounted-for water. If there are two meters with the same percentage, the program will pick the meter with the greatest percentage of flow in the normal range. If this, too, is a tie, it will default to the meter with the lowest head loss at maximum-recorded flow. Each meter option's projected performance can be further analyzed on the graphical analysis screen.

6. Graphical Analysis

The actual demand data can be viewed graphically against the specified flow ranges for each meter type and size option (Figure A-4). This enables the user to determine whether or not a recommended meter option is too small based on peak flow and the percentage of flow outside a meter's normal (optimal) flow range.

7. Calibration of Results

Meter sizing software permits very complex and time-consuming calculating to be performed quickly and accurately. It is only a tool, however, to assist the user in a final decision that often must take into consideration other factors, such as fire-flow requirements and possible changes in demand due to many possible causes. Also, no model is perfect. If the users are unsure about any of the assumptions, they may run the analysis using best and worst case scenarios to determine the range of possible outcomes. For example, if they are unsure of relative meter maintenance costs or wish to vary assumptions for accounted-for water below specified minimum and above maximum flow rates, they may run the analysis using different values. It is recommended that the user try different scenarios in order to better understand the potential deviation of results obtained through any model.

In many cases, people are surprised at the potential for downsizing and will often opt for a meter smaller than the existing meter, yet larger than the optimum calculated by a software model. Meter sizing software allows the user to evaluate all potential scenarios and their consequences. In cases where a more conservative decision is either preferred or required due to specific considerations such as fire flows, the program provides a good indication of the cost (lost-revenue potential) associated with such a decision.

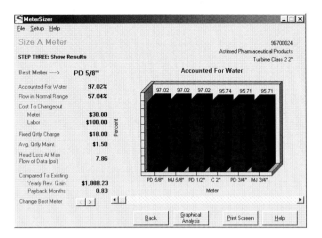

Figure A-3   Initial results screen (sample from *MeterSizer*®)

Courtesy of F.S. Brainard and Co.

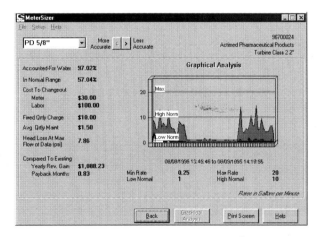

Figure A-4   Graphic analysis screen (sample from *MeterSizer*®)

Courtesy of F.S. Brainard and Co.

This page intentionally blank.

Appendix B

Flow Friction Loss Tables

The following tables (Tables B-1 through B-39) contain friction loss values for common service line materials (copper, polyethylene, PEX and PVC) and sizes (¾-in. to 8-in. diameter). The friction loss values are given in pounds per square inch (psi) pressure loss per 100 ft of pipe. The tables include only standard inside diameters. For other pipe materials and sizes, the friction loss values can be calculated from the Hazen–Williams formula by substituting the corresponding constants and values.

The tables contain the velocity of water in feet per second (ft/sec) for corresponding head-loss values that will be required in selecting the proper size service for the flow. High velocities can cause excessive water hammer (when valves are closed rapidly) and, in some cases, cavitation damage to service material. It is recommended that the maximum water velocity in the service be not more than 10 ft/sec. Higher values are listed in the tables for the engineer's use, but these do not constitute a recommendation for the use of high velocities.

Table B-1   Copper water tube properties—C=130—¾ in. nominal diameter

C = 130	ID = Inside Diameter*					
	Type K ID = 0.745		Type L ID = 0.785		Type M ID = 0.811	
Flow, *gpm*	Head Loss, *ft/100 ft*	Velocity, *ft/s*	Head Loss, *ft/100 ft*	Velocity, *ft/s*	Head Loss, *ft/100 ft*	Velocity, *ft/s*
1	0.53	0.74	0.41	0.66	0.35	0.62
2	1.92	1.47	1.49	1.33	1.27	1.24
3	4.07	2.21	3.16	1.99	2.69	1.86
4	6.93	2.94	5.38	2.65	4.59	2.48
5	10.48	3.68	8.13	3.31	6.93	3.11
6	14.69	4.42	11.39	3.98	9.72	3.73
7	19.55	5.15	15.15	4.64	12.93	4.35
8	25.03	5.89	19.40	5.30	16.55	4.97
9	31.13	6.62	24.13	5.97	20.59	5.59
10	37.84	7.36	29.33	6.63	25.03	6.21
11	45.14	8.10	34.99	7.29	29.86	6.83
12	53.04	8.83	41.11	7.95	35.08	7.45

* ASTM B88 standard.

(Table continued next page.)

Table B-1   Copper water tube properties—C=130—¾ in. nominal diameter (continued)

C = 130	ID = Inside Diameter*					
	Type K ID = 0.745		Type L ID = 0.785		Type M ID = 0.811	
Flow, gpm	Head Loss, ft/100 ft	Velocity, ft/s	Head Loss, ft/100 ft	Velocity, ft/s	Head Loss, ft/100 ft	Velocity, ft/s
13	61.51	9.57	47.68	8.62	40.68	8.07
14	70.56	10.30	54.69	9.28	46.67	8.70
15			62.14	9.94	53.03	9.32
16			70.03	10.61	59.76	9.94
17					66.86	10.56

* ASTM B88 standard.

Table B-2   Copper water tube properties—C=130—1 in. nominal diameter

C = 130	ID = Inside Diameter*					
	Type K ID = 0.995		Type L ID = 1.025		Type M ID = 1.055	
Flow, gpm	Head Loss, ft/100 ft	Velocity, ft/s	Head Loss, ft/100 ft	Velocity, ft/s	Head Loss, ft/100 ft	Velocity, ft/s
2	0.47	0.83	0.41	0.78	0.35	0.73
3	0.99	1.24	0.86	1.17	0.75	1.10
4	1.69	1.65	1.47	1.56	1.27	1.47
5	2.56	2.06	2.22	1.94	1.93	1.84
6	3.59	2.48	3.11	2.33	2.70	2.20
7	4.78	2.89	4.13	2.72	3.59	2.57
8	6.12	3.30	5.29	3.11	4.60	2.94
9	7.61	3.71	6.58	3.50	5.72	3.30
10	9.24	4.13	8.00	3.89	6.95	3.67
12	12.96	4.95	11.21	4.67	9.74	4.40
14	17.24	5.78	14.92	5.44	12.96	5.14
16	22.07	6.60	19.10	6.22	16.60	5.87
18	27.45	7.43	23.76	7.00	20.64	6.61
20	33.37	8.25	28.87	7.78	25.09	7.34
25	50.44	10.32	43.65	9.72	37.93	9.18
30			61.18	11.66	53.16	11.01

* ASTM B88 standard.

Table B-3   Copper water tube properties—C=130—1¼ in. nominal diameter

C = 130	ID = Inside diameter*					
	Type K ID = 1.245		Type L ID = 1.265		Type M ID = 1.291	
Flow, gpm	Head Loss, ft/100 ft	Velocity, ft/s	Head Loss, ft/100 ft	Velocity, ft/s	Head Loss, ft/100 ft	Velocity, ft/s
5	0.86	1.32	0.80	1.28	0.72	1.23
6	1.20	1.58	1.11	1.53	1.01	1.47
7	1.60	1.84	1.48	1.79	1.34	1.72
8	2.05	2.11	1.90	2.04	1.72	1.96
9	2.55	2.37	2.36	2.30	2.14	2.21
10	3.10	2.64	2.87	2.55	2.60	2.45
12	4.35	3.16	4.02	3.06	3.64	2.94
15	6.57	3.95	6.08	3.83	5.51	3.68
20	11.20	5.27	10.36	5.11	9.39	4.90
25	16.93	6.59	15.67	6.38	14.19	6.13
30	23.73	7.91	21.96	7.66	19.89	7.35
35	31.57	9.22	29.21	8.93	26.46	8.58
40	40.43	10.54	37.41	10.21	33.88	9.80
45					42.14	11.03

*ASTM B88 standard.

Table B-4   Copper water tube properties—C=130—1½ in. nominal diameter

C = 130	ID = Inside Diameter*					
	Type K ID = 1.481		Type L ID = 1.505		Type M ID = 1.527	
Flow, gpm	Head Loss, ft/100 ft	Velocity, ft/s	Head Loss, ft/100 ft	Velocity, ft/s	Head Loss, ft/100 ft	Velocity ft/s
8	0.88	1.49	0.81	1.44	0.76	1.40
9	1.10	1.68	1.01	1.62	0.94	1.58
10	1.33	1.86	1.23	1.80	1.15	1.75
12	1.87	2.23	1.73	2.16	1.61	2.10
15	2.82	2.79	2.61	2.71	2.43	2.63
20	4.81	3.72	4.45	3.61	4.14	3.50
25	7.27	4.66	6.72	4.51	6.26	4.38
30	10.19	5.59	9.42	5.41	8.78	5.26
35	13.56	6.52	12.54	6.31	11.68	6.13
40	17.36	7.45	16.05	7.21	14.96	7.01
45	21.59	8.38	19.97	8.12	18.60	7.88
50	26.24	9.31	24.27	9.02	22.61	8.76
60	36.78	11.17	34.01	10.82	31.69	10.51

* ASTM B88 standard.

Table B-5   Copper water tube properties—C=130—2 in. nominal diameter

C = 130	ID = Inside Diameter*					
	Type K ID = 1.959		Type L ID = 1.985		Type M ID = 2.009	
Flow, *gpm*	Head Loss *ft/100 ft*	Velocity, *ft/s*	Head Loss, *ft/100 ft*	Velocity, *ft/s*	Head Loss, *ft/100 ft*	Velocity, *ft/s*
10	0.34	1.06	0.32	1.04	0.30	1.01
12	0.48	1.28	0.45	1.24	0.42	1.21
14	0.64	1.49	0.60	1.45	0.56	1.42
16	0.81	1.70	0.76	1.66	0.72	1.62
18	1.01	1.92	0.95	1.87	0.90	1.82
20	1.23	2.13	1.15	2.07	1.09	2.02
25	1.86	2.66	1.75	2.59	1.65	2.53
30	2.61	3.19	2.45	3.11	2.31	3.04
35	3.47	3.73	3.26	3.63	3.07	3.54
40	4.45	4.26	4.17	4.15	3.93	4.05
45	5.53	4.79	5.18	4.67	4.89	4.55
50	6.72	5.32	6.30	5.18	5.94	5.06
60	9.42	6.39	8.83	6.22	8.33	6.07
70	12.53	7.45	11.75	7.26	11.08	7.08
80	16.05	8.52	15.05	8.29	14.19	8.10
90	19.96	9.58	18.72	9.33	17.65	9.11
100	24.26	10.64	22.75	10.37	21.45	10.12

*ASTM B88 standard.

Table B-6   Copper water tube properties—C=130—2½ in. nominal diameter

C = 130	ID = Inside Diameter*					
	Type K ID = 2.435		Type L ID = 2.465		Type M ID = 2.495	
Flow, *gpm*	Head Loss, *ft/100 ft*	Velocity, *ft/s*	Head Loss, *ft/100 ft*	Velocity, *ft/s*	Head Loss, *ft/100 ft*	Velocity, *ft/s*
20	0.43	1.38	0.40	1.34	0.38	1.31
25	0.65	1.72	0.61	1.68	0.57	1.64
30	0.90	2.07	0.85	2.02	0.80	1.97
35	1.20	2.41	1.13	2.35	1.07	2.30
40	1.54	2.76	1.45	2.69	1.37	2.62
45	1.92	3.10	1.81	3.03	1.70	2.95
50	2.33	3.44	2.19	3.36	2.07	3.28
60	3.27	4.13	3.08	4.03	2.90	3.94
70	4.34	4.82	4.09	4.71	3.86	4.59
80	5.56	5.51	5.24	5.38	4.94	5.25
90	6.92	6.20	6.52	6.05	6.14	5.91
100	8.41	6.89	7.92	6.72	7.47	6.56
110	10.03	7.58	9.45	7.40	8.91	7.22
120	11.79	8.27	11.10	8.07	10.47	7.87
130	13.67	8.96	12.88	8.74	12.14	8.53
140	15.68	9.65	14.77	9.41	13.93	9.19

* ASTM B88 standard.   *(Table continued next page.)*

Table B-6   Copper water tube properties—*C*=130—2½ in. nominal diameter (continued)

C = 130	ID = Inside Diameter*					
	Type K ID = 2.435		Type L ID = 2.465		Type M ID = 2.495	
Flow, *gpm*	Head Loss, *ft/100 ft*	Velocity, *ft/s*	Head Loss, *ft/100 ft*	Velocity, *ft/s*	Head Loss, *ft/100 ft*	Velocity, *ft/s*
150	17.82	10.33	16.79	10.08	15.83	9.84
160	20.08	11.02	18.92	10.76	17.83	10.50

* ASTM B88 standard.

Table B-7   Copper water tube properties—*C*=130—3 in. nominal diameter

C = 130	ID = Inside Diameter*					
	Type K ID = 2.907		Type L ID = 2.945		Type M ID = 2.981	
Flow, *gpm*	Head Loss, *ft/100 ft*	Velocity, *ft/s*	Head Loss, *ft/100 ft*	Velocity, *ft/s*	Head Loss, *ft/100 ft*	Velocity, *ft/s*
20	0.18	0.97	0.17	0.94	0.16	0.92
30	0.38	1.45	0.36	1.41	0.34	1.38
40	0.65	1.93	0.61	1.88	0.58	1.84
50	0.98	2.42	0.92	2.35	0.87	2.30
60	1.38	2.90	1.29	2.83	1.22	2.76
70	1.83	3.38	1.72	3.30	1.62	3.22
80	2.35	3.87	2.20	3.77	2.08	3.68
90	2.92	4.35	2.74	4.24	2.58	4.14
100	3.55	4.83	3.33	4.71	3.14	4.60
110	4.23	5.32	3.97	5.18	3.75	5.06
120	4.97	5.80	4.67	5.65	4.40	5.52
130	5.77	6.28	5.41	6.12	5.10	5.98
140	6.62	6.77	6.21	6.59	5.85	6.44
150	7.52	7.25	7.06	7.06	6.65	6.90
160	8.47	7.73	7.95	7.54	7.50	7.36
170	9.48	8.22	8.90	8.01	8.39	7.81
180	10.54	8.70	9.89	8.48	9.32	8.27
190	11.65	9.18	10.93	8.95	10.30	8.73
200	12.81	9.67	12.02	9.42	11.33	9.19
210	14.02	10.15	13.16	9.89	12.40	9.65
220	15.28	10.63	14.34	10.36	13.52	10.11

* ASTM B88 standard.

Table B-8   Copper water tube properties—*C*=130—3½ in. nominal diameter

C = 130	ID = Inside Diameter*					
	Type K ID = 3.385		Type L ID = 3.425		Type M ID = 3.459	
Flow, *gpm*	Head Loss, *ft/100 ft*	Velocity, *ft/s*	Head Loss, *ft/100 ft*	Velocity, *ft/s*	Head Loss, *ft/100 ft*	Velocity, *ft/s*
60	0.66	2.14	0.62	2.09	0.59	2.05
70	0.87	2.50	0.82	2.44	0.79	2.39
80	1.12	2.85	1.06	2.79	1.01	2.73
90	1.39	3.21	1.31	3.13	1.25	3.07
100	1.69	3.57	1.60	3.48	1.52	3.41
110	2.02	3.92	1.90	3.83	1.82	3.76
120	2.37	4.28	2.24	4.18	2.13	4.10
130	2.75	4.63	2.60	4.53	2.47	4.44
140	3.15	4.99	2.98	4.88	2.84	4.78
150	3.58	5.35	3.38	5.22	3.22	5.12
160	4.04	5.70	3.81	5.57	3.63	5.46
170	4.52	6.06	4.26	5.92	4.06	5.80
180	5.02	6.42	4.74	6.27	4.52	6.15
190	5.55	6.77	5.24	6.62	4.99	6.49
200	6.10	7.13	5.76	6.96	5.49	6.83
220	7.28	7.84	6.87	7.66	6.55	7.51
240	8.55	8.56	8.08	8.36	7.70	8.19
260	9.92	9.27	9.37	9.05	8.93	8.88
280	11.38	9.98	10.75	9.75	10.24	9.56
300	12.93	10.70	12.21	10.45	11.64	10.24

* ASTM B88 standard.

Table B-9   Copper water tube properties—*C*=130—4 in. nominal diameter

C = 130	ID = Inside Diameter*					
	Type K ID = 3.857		Type L ID = 3.905		Type M ID = 3.935	
Flow, *gpm*	Head Loss, *ft/100 ft*	Velocity, *ft/s*	Head Loss, *ft/100 ft*	Velocity, *ft/s*	Head Loss, *ft/100 ft*	Velocity, *ft/s*
100	0.90	2.75	0.84	2.68	0.81	2.64
110	1.07	3.02	1.01	2.95	0.97	2.90
120	1.25	3.30	1.18	3.21	1.14	3.17
130	1.46	3.57	1.37	3.48	1.32	3.43
140	1.67	3.84	1.57	3.75	1.51	3.69
150	1.90	4.12	1.79	4.02	1.72	3.96
160	2.14	4.39	2.01	4.29	1.94	4.22
170	2.39	4.67	2.25	4.55	2.17	4.48
180	2.66	4.94	2.50	4.82	2.41	4.75
190	2.94	5.22	2.77	5.09	2.67	5.01
200	3.23	5.49	3.04	5.36	2.93	5.28
220	3.85	6.04	3.63	5.89	3.50	5.80
240	4.53	6.59	4.26	6.43	4.11	6.33

* ASTM B88 standard.   *(Table continued next page.)*

Table B-9 Copper water tube properties—*C*=130—4 in. nominal diameter (continued)

| C = 130 | ID = Inside Diameter* | | | | | |
| | Type K ID = 3.857 | | Type L ID = 3.905 | | Type M ID = 3.935 | |
Flow, *gpm*	Head Loss, *ft/100 ft*	Velocity, *ft/s*	Head Loss, *ft/100 ft*	Velocity, *ft/s*	Head Loss, *ft/100 ft*	Velocity, *ft/s*
260	5.25	7.14	4.95	6.97	4.76	6.86
280	6.02	7.69	5.67	7.50	5.47	7.39
300	6.85	8.24	6.45	8.04	6.21	7.91
350	9.11	9.61	8.58	9.38	8.26	9.23
400	11.66	10.98	10.98	10.72	10.58	10.55

* ASTM B88 standard.

Table B-10 Copper water tube properties—*C*=130—5 in. nominal diameter

| C = 130 | ID = Inside Diameter* | | | | | |
| | Type K ID = 4.805 | | Type L ID = 4.875 | | Type M ID = 4.907 | |
Flow, *gpm*	Head Loss, *ft/100 ft*	Velocity, *ft/s*	Head Loss, *ft/100 ft*	Velocity, *ft/s*	Head Loss, *ft/100 ft*	Velocity, **ft/s**
150	0.65	2.65	0.61	2.58	0.59	2.54
160	0.73	2.83	0.68	2.75	0.66	2.71
170	0.82	3.01	0.76	2.92	0.74	2.88
180	0.91	3.18	0.85	3.09	0.82	3.05
190	1.01	3.36	0.94	3.27	0.91	3.22
200	1.11	3.54	1.03	3.44	1.00	3.39
220	1.32	3.89	1.23	3.78	1.19	3.73
240	1.55	4.25	1.45	4.13	1.40	4.07
260	1.80	4.60	1.68	4.47	1.63	4.41
280	2.07	4.95	1.93	4.81	1.86	4.75
300	2.35	5.31	2.19	5.16	2.12	5.09
350	3.12	6.19	2.91	6.02	2.82	5.94
400	4.00	7.08	3.73	6.88	3.61	6.79
450	4.97	7.96	4.64	7.73	4.49	7.63
500	6.05	8.85	5.63	8.59	5.46	8.48
550	7.21	9.73	6.72	9.45	6.51	9.33
600	8.47	10.62	7.90	10.31	7.65	10.18

* ASTM B88 standard.

Table B-11 Copper water tube properties—C=130—6 in. nominal diameter

C = 130	ID = Inside Diameter*					
	Type K ID = 5.741		Type L ID = 5.845		Type M ID = 5.881	
Flow, gpm	Head Loss, ft/100 ft	Velocity, ft/s	Head Loss, ft/100 ft	Velocity, ft/s	Head Loss, ft/100 ft	Velocity, ft/s
240	0.65	2.97	0.60	2.87	0.58	2.83
260	0.76	3.22	0.69	3.11	0.67	3.07
280	0.87	3.47	0.80	3.35	0.77	3.31
300	0.99	3.72	0.90	3.59	0.88	3.54
350	1.31	4.34	1.20	4.18	1.17	4.13
400	1.68	4.96	1.54	4.78	1.49	4.72
450	2.09	5.58	1.92	5.38	1.86	5.31
500	2.54	6.20	2.33	5.98	2.26	5.91
550	3.03	6.82	2.78	6.58	2.70	6.50
600	3.56	7.44	3.26	7.17	3.17	7.09
650	4.13	8.06	3.78	7.77	3.67	7.68
700	4.74	8.68	4.34	8.37	4.21	8.27
750	5.38	9.30	4.93	8.97	4.79	8.86
800	6.07	9.92	5.56	9.57	5.40	9.45
850	6.79	10.53	6.22	10.16	6.04	10.04

* ASTM B88 standard.

Table B-12 Copper water tube properties—C=130—8 in. nominal diameter

C = 130	ID = Inside Diameter*					
	Type K ID = 7.583		Type L ID = 7.725		Type M ID = 7.785	
Flow, gpm	Head Loss, ft/100 ft	Velocity, ft/s	Head Loss, ft/100 ft	Velocity, ft/s	Head Loss, ft/100 ft	Velocity, ft/s
500	0.66	3.55	0.60	3.42	0.58	3.37
550	0.78	3.91	0.71	3.76	0.69	3.71
600	0.92	4.26	0.84	4.11	0.81	4.04
650	1.07	4.62	0.97	4.45	0.94	4.38
700	1.22	4.97	1.12	4.79	1.07	4.72
750	1.39	5.33	1.27	5.13	1.22	5.06
800	1.56	5.68	1.43	5.48	1.38	5.39
850	1.75	6.04	1.60	5.82	1.54	5.73
900	1.95	6.39	1.78	6.16	1.71	6.07
950	2.15	6.75	1.96	6.50	1.89	6.40
1000	2.37	7.10	2.16	6.85	2.08	6.74
1100	2.82	7.81	2.58	7.53	2.48	7.41
1200	3.31	8.52	3.03	8.21	2.92	8.09
1300	3.84	9.24	3.51	8.90	3.38	8.76
1400	4.41	9.95	4.03	9.58	3.88	9.44
1500	5.01	10.66	4.58	10.27	4.41	10.11

* ASTM B88 standard.

Table B-13   Polyvinyl chloride (PVC) pipe—*C*=130—¾ in. nominal diameter

C = 130	ID = Inside Diameter*					
	SDR17 ID = 0.886		SDR21 ID = 0.89		SDR26 ID = N/A†	
Flow, *gpm*	Head Loss, *ft/100 ft*	Velocity, *ft/s*	Head Loss, *ft/100 ft*	Velocity, *ft/s*	Head Loss, *ft/100 ft*	Velocity, *ft/s*
1	0.23	0.52	0.22	0.52	N/A	N/A
2	0.83	1.04	0.81	1.03	N/A	N/A
3	1.75	1.56	1.71	1.55	N/A	N/A
4	2.98	2.08	2.92	2.06	N/A	N/A
5	4.51	2.60	4.41	2.58	N/A	N/A
6	6.32	3.12	6.18	3.09	N/A	N/A
7	8.40	3.64	8.22	3.61	N/A	N/A
8	10.76	4.16	10.53	4.13	N/A	N/A
9	13.38	4.68	13.09	4.64	N/A	N/A
10	16.27	5.20	15.91	5.16	N/A	N/A
11	19.41	5.72	18.99	5.67	N/A	N/A
12	22.80	6.24	22.31	6.19	N/A	N/A
13	26.44	6.76	25.87	6.70	N/A	N/A
14	30.33	7.29	29.67	7.22	N/A	N/A
15	34.47	7.81	33.72	7.74	N/A	N/A
16	38.84	8.33	38.00	8.25	N/A	N/A
17	43.46	8.85	42.51	8.77	N/A	N/A
18	48.31	9.37	47.26	9.28	N/A	N/A
19	53.40	9.89	52.24	9.80	N/A	N/A
20	58.72	10.41	57.44	10.31	N/A	N/A

* ASTM D2241.
† NA = not applicable.

Table B-14   PVC pipe—*C*=130—1 in. nominal diameter

C = 130	ID = Inside Diameter*					
	SDR17 ID = 1.121		SDR21 ID = 1.149		SDR26 ID = 1.155	
Flow, *gpm*	Head Loss, *ft/100 ft*	Velocity, *ft/s*	Head Loss, *ft/100 ft*	Velocity, *ft/s*	Head Loss, *ft/100 ft*	Velocity, *ft/s*
1	0.07	0.33	0.06	0.31	0.06	0.31
2	0.26	0.65	0.23	0.62	0.23	0.61
3	0.56	0.98	0.49	0.93	0.48	0.92
4	0.95	1.30	0.84	1.24	0.82	1.22
5	1.43	1.63	1.27	1.55	1.24	1.53
6	2.01	1.95	1.78	1.86	1.74	1.84
7	2.67	2.28	2.37	2.17	2.31	2.14
8	3.42	2.60	3.03	2.48	2.96	2.45
9	4.26	2.93	3.77	2.78	3.68	2.76
10	5.17	3.25	4.59	3.09	4.47	3.06
12	7.25	3.90	6.43	3.71	6.27	3.67
14	9.64	4.55	8.55	4.33	8.34	4.29

* ASTM D2241.   *(Table continued next page.)*

Table B-14   PVC pipe—C=130—1 in. nominal diameter (continued)

| C = 130 | ID = Inside Diameter* | | | | | |
| | SDR17 ID = 1.121 | | SDR21 ID = 1.149 | | SDR26 ID = 1.155 | |
Flow, gpm	Head Loss, ft/100 ft	Velocity, ft/s	Head Loss, ft/100 ft	Velocity, ft/s	Head Loss, ft/100 ft	Velocity, ft/s
16	12.35	5.20	10.95	4.95	10.68	4.90
18	15.36	5.85	13.62	5.57	13.28	5.51
20	18.67	6.50	16.56	6.19	16.14	6.12
25	28.22	8.13	25.03	7.74	24.40	7.66
30	39.56	9.75	35.08	9.28	34.20	9.19
35	52.63	11.38	46.67	10.83	45.50	10.72

* ASTM D2241.

Table B-15   PVC pipe—C=130—1¼ in. nominal diameter

| C = 130 | ID = Inside Diameter* | | | | | |
| | SDR17 ID = 1.424 | | SDR21 ID = 1.462 | | SDR26 ID = 1.492 | |
Flow, gpm	Head Loss, ft/100 ft	Velocity, ft/s	Head Loss, ft/100 ft	Velocity, ft/s	Head Loss, ft/100 ft	Velocity, ft/s
5	0.45	1.01	0.39	0.96	0.36	0.92
6	0.63	1.21	0.55	1.15	0.50	1.10
7	0.83	1.41	0.73	1.34	0.66	1.28
8	1.07	1.61	0.94	1.53	0.85	1.47
9	1.33	1.81	1.17	1.72	1.06	1.65
10	1.61	2.01	1.42	1.91	1.29	1.84
12	2.26	2.42	1.99	2.29	1.80	2.20
15	3.42	3.02	3.01	2.87	2.72	2.75
20	5.82	4.03	5.12	3.82	4.64	3.67
25	8.80	5.04	7.74	4.78	7.01	4.59
30	12.34	6.04	10.85	5.73	9.83	5.51
35	16.41	7.05	14.44	6.69	13.08	6.42
40	21.02	8.06	18.49	7.64	16.75	7.34
45	26.14	9.07	22.99	8.60	20.83	8.26
50	31.77	10.07	27.95	9.56	25.31	9.18
55			33.34	10.51	30.20	10.09

* ASTM D2241.

Table B-16 PVC pipe—*C*=130—1½ in. nominal diameter

C = 130	ID = Inside Diameter*					
	SDR17 ID = 1.636		SDR21 ID = 1.68		SDR26 ID = 1.714	
Flow, *gpm*	Head Loss, *ft/100 ft*	Velocity, *ft/s*	Head Loss, *ft/100 ft*	Velocity, *ft/s*	Head Loss, *ft/100 ft*	Velocity, **ft/s**
8	0.54	1.22	0.48	1.16	0.43	1.11
9	0.68	1.37	0.59	1.30	0.54	1.25
10	0.82	1.53	0.72	1.45	0.65	1.39
12	1.15	1.83	1.01	1.74	0.92	1.67
15	1.74	2.29	1.53	2.17	1.39	2.09
20	2.96	3.05	2.60	2.89	2.36	2.78
25	4.48	3.82	3.93	3.62	3.57	3.48
30	6.28	4.58	5.51	4.34	5.00	4.17
35	8.35	5.34	7.34	5.07	6.65	4.87
40	10.69	6.10	9.39	5.79	8.52	5.56
50	16.16	7.63	14.20	7.24	12.88	6.95
60	22.65	9.16	19.91	8.68	18.05	8.34
70	30.14	10.68	26.48	10.13	24.02	9.73
80					30.76	11.12

* ASTM D2241.

Table B-17 PVC pipe—*C*=130—2 in. nominal diameter

C = 130	ID = Inside Diameter*					
	SDR17 ID = 2.055		SDR21 ID = 2.109		SDR26 ID = 2.153	
Flow, *gpm*	Head Loss, *ft/100 ft*	Velocity, *ft/s*	Head Loss, *ft/100 ft*	Velocity, *ft/s*	Head Loss, *ft/100 ft*	Velocity, *ft/s*
10	0.27	0.97	0.24	0.92	0.22	0.88
12	0.38	1.16	0.33	1.10	0.30	1.06
14	0.50	1.35	0.44	1.29	0.40	1.23
16	0.65	1.55	0.57	1.47	0.51	1.41
18	0.80	1.74	0.71	1.65	0.64	1.59
20	0.98	1.93	0.86	1.84	0.78	1.76
25	1.47	2.42	1.30	2.30	1.18	2.20
30	2.07	2.90	1.82	2.76	1.65	2.64
35	2.75	3.39	2.42	3.21	2.19	3.08
40	3.52	3.87	3.10	3.67	2.81	3.53
45	4.38	4.35	3.86	4.13	3.49	3.97
50	5.32	4.84	4.69	4.59	4.24	4.41
60	7.46	5.80	6.58	5.51	5.95	5.29
70	9.93	6.77	8.75	6.43	7.91	6.17
80	12.71	7.74	11.20	7.35	10.13	7.05
90	15.81	8.71	13.93	8.27	12.60	7.93
100	19.21	9.67	16.93	9.18	15.31	8.81
110	22.92	10.64	20.20	10.10	18.27	9.69
120					21.46	10.58

* ASTM D2241.

Table B-18   PVC pipe—*C*=130—2½ in. nominal diameter

C = 130	ID = Inside Diameter*					
	SDR17 ID = 2.497		SDR21 ID = 2.561		SDR26 ID = 2.615	
Flow, gpm	Head Loss, ft/100 ft	Velocity, ft/s	Head Loss, ft/100 ft	Velocity, ft/s	Head Loss, ft/100 ft	Velocity, ft/s
20	0.38	1.31	0.33	1.25	0.30	1.19
25	0.57	1.64	0.50	1.56	0.46	1.49
30	0.80	1.97	0.71	1.87	0.64	1.79
35	1.06	2.29	0.94	2.18	0.85	2.09
40	1.36	2.62	1.21	2.49	1.09	2.39
45	1.70	2.95	1.50	2.80	1.35	2.69
50	2.06	3.28	1.82	3.11	1.65	2.99
60	2.89	3.93	2.55	3.74	2.31	3.58
70	3.84	4.59	3.40	4.36	3.07	4.18
80	4.92	5.24	4.35	4.98	3.93	4.78
90	6.12	5.90	5.41	5.61	4.89	5.38
100	7.44	6.55	6.58	6.23	5.94	5.97
110	8.88	7.21	7.85	6.85	7.09	6.57
120	10.43	7.86	9.22	7.47	8.33	7.17
130	12.09	8.52	10.69	8.10	9.66	7.77
140	13.87	9.17	12.26	8.72	11.08	8.36
150	15.76	9.83	13.94	9.34	12.59	8.96
160	17.76	10.48	15.70	9.97	14.19	9.56
170			17.57	10.59	15.87	10.16

* ASTM D2241.

Table B-19   PVC pipe—*C*=130—3 in. nominal diameter

C = 130	ID = Inside Diameter*					
	SDR17 ID = 3.038		SDR21 ID = 3.126		SDR26 ID = 3.19	
Flow, gpm	Head Loss, ft/100 ft	Velocity, ft/s	Head Loss, ft/100 ft	Velocity, ft/s	Head Loss, ft/100 ft	Velocity, ft/s
20	0.15	0.89	0.13	0.84	0.11	0.80
30	0.31	1.33	0.27	1.25	0.24	1.20
40	0.52	1.77	0.46	1.67	0.41	1.61
50	0.79	2.21	0.69	2.09	0.63	2.01
60	1.11	2.66	0.97	2.51	0.88	2.41
70	1.48	3.10	1.29	2.93	1.17	2.81
80	1.89	3.54	1.65	3.34	1.49	3.21
90	2.36	3.98	2.05	3.76	1.86	3.61
100	2.86	4.43	2.49	4.18	2.26	4.01
110	3.42	4.87	2.97	4.60	2.69	4.42
120	4.01	5.31	3.49	5.02	3.16	4.82
130	4.65	5.75	4.05	5.43	3.67	5.22
140	5.34	6.20	4.64	5.85	4.21	5.62
150	6.07	6.64	5.28	6.27	4.78	6.02

* ASTM D2241.

(Table continued next page.)

Table B-19   PVC pipe—C=130—3 in. nominal diameter (continued)

$C = 130$	ID = Inside Diameter*					
	SDR17 ID = 3.038		SDR21 ID = 3.126		SDR26 ID = 3.19	
Flow, gpm	Head Loss, ft/100 ft	Velocity, ft/s	Head Loss, ft/100 ft	Velocity, ft/s	Head Loss, ft/100 ft	Velocity, ft/s
160	6.84	7.08	5.95	6.69	5.39	6.42
170	7.65	7.52	6.65	7.11	6.03	6.82
180	8.50	7.97	7.40	7.52	6.70	7.23
190	9.40	8.41	8.18	7.94	7.41	7.63
200	10.33	8.85	8.99	8.36	8.15	8.03
210	11.31	9.29	9.84	8.78	8.92	8.43
220	12.33	9.74	10.73	9.20	9.72	8.83
230	13.39	10.18	11.65	9.61	10.55	9.23
240			12.60	10.03	11.42	9.63
250					12.31	10.04

* ASTM D2241.

Table B-20   PVC pipe—C=130—3½ in. nominal diameter

$C = 130$	ID = Inside Diameter*					
	SDR17 ID = 3.474		SDR21 ID = 3.574		SDR26 ID = 3.652	
Flow, gpm	Head Loss, ft/100 ft	Velocity, ft/s	Head Loss, ft/100 ft	Velocity, ft/s	Head Loss, ft/100 ft	Velocity, ft/s
60	0.58	2.03	0.50	1.92	0.45	1.84
70	0.77	2.37	0.67	2.24	0.60	2.14
80	0.99	2.71	0.86	2.56	0.77	2.45
90	1.23	3.05	1.07	2.88	0.96	2.76
100	1.49	3.38	1.30	3.20	1.17	3.06
110	1.78	3.72	1.55	3.52	1.39	3.37
120	2.09	4.06	1.82	3.84	1.64	3.68
130	2.42	4.40	2.11	4.16	1.90	3.98
140	2.78	4.74	2.42	4.48	2.18	4.29
150	3.16	5.08	2.75	4.80	2.47	4.59
160	3.56	5.42	3.10	5.12	2.79	4.90
170	3.98	5.75	3.47	5.44	3.12	5.21
180	4.42	6.09	3.85	5.76	3.47	5.51
190	4.89	6.43	4.26	6.08	3.83	5.82
200	5.38	6.77	4.68	6.40	4.22	6.13
220	6.42	7.45	5.59	7.04	5.03	6.74
240	7.54	8.12	6.56	7.68	5.91	7.35
260	8.74	8.80	7.61	8.31	6.85	7.96
280	10.03	9.48	8.73	8.95	7.86	8.58
300	11.39	10.15	9.92	9.59	8.93	9.19
320			11.18	10.23	10.07	9.80
340					11.26	10.41

* ASTM D2241.

Table B-21   PVC pipe—*C*=130—4 in. nominal diameter

Flow, gpm	SDR14 ID = 4.114		SDR18 ID = 4.266		SDR25 ID = 4.116	
	Head Loss, ft/100 ft	Velocity, ft/s	Head Loss, ft/100 ft	Velocity, ft/s	Head Loss, ft/100 ft	Velocity, ft/s
100	0.65	2.41	0.55	2.24	0.65	2.41
110	0.78	2.65	0.65	2.47	0.78	2.65
120	0.92	2.90	0.77	2.69	0.91	2.89
130	1.06	3.14	0.89	2.92	1.06	3.13
140	1.22	3.38	1.02	3.14	1.22	3.38
150	1.39	3.62	1.16	3.37	1.38	3.62
160	1.56	3.86	1.31	3.59	1.56	3.86
170	1.75	4.10	1.46	3.82	1.74	4.10
180	1.94	4.34	1.63	4.04	1.94	4.34
190	2.15	4.59	1.80	4.26	2.14	4.58
200	2.36	4.83	1.98	4.49	2.35	4.82
220	2.82	5.31	2.36	4.94	2.81	5.30
240	3.31	5.79	2.77	5.39	3.30	5.79
260	3.84	6.28	3.21	5.84	3.83	6.27
280	4.40	6.76	3.69	6.29	4.39	6.75
300	5.00	7.24	4.19	6.73	4.99	7.23
350	6.65	8.45	5.57	7.86	6.64	8.44
400	8.52	9.65	7.14	8.98	8.50	9.64
450					10.57	10.85

* AWWA C900-97.

Table B-22   PVC pipe—*C*=130—5 in. nominal diameter

Flow, gpm	SDR17 ID = 4.831		SDR21 ID = 4.969		SDR26 ID = 5.081	
	Head Loss, ft/100 ft	Velocity, ft/s	Head Loss, ft/100 ft	Velocity, ft/s	Head Loss, ft/100 ft	Velocity, ft/s
150	0.63	2.63	0.55	2.48	0.50	2.37
160	0.71	2.80	0.62	2.65	0.56	2.53
170	0.80	2.98	0.70	2.81	0.62	2.69
180	0.89	3.15	0.77	2.98	0.69	2.85
190	0.98	3.33	0.86	3.14	0.77	3.01
200	1.08	3.50	0.94	3.31	0.84	3.16
220	1.29	3.85	1.12	3.64	1.01	3.48
240	1.51	4.20	1.32	3.97	1.18	3.80
260	1.75	4.55	1.53	4.30	1.37	4.11
280	2.01	4.90	1.75	4.63	1.57	4.43
300	2.29	5.25	1.99	4.96	1.79	4.75
350	3.04	6.13	2.65	5.79	2.38	5.54
400	3.90	7.00	3.40	6.62	3.05	6.33
450	4.84	7.88	4.22	7.44	3.79	7.12

* ASTM D2241.

(Table continued next page.)

Table B-22   PVC pipe—C=130—5 in. nominal diameter (continued)

| C = 130 | ID = Inside Diameter* | | | | | |
| | SDR17 ID = 4.831 | | SDR21 ID = 4.969 | | SDR26 ID = 5.081 | |
Flow, gpm	Head Loss, ft/100 ft	Velocity, ft/s	Head Loss, ft/100 ft	Velocity, ft/s	Head Loss, ft/100 ft	Velocity, ft/s
500	5.89	8.75	5.13	8.27	4.61	7.91
550	7.03	9.63	6.12	9.10	5.49	8.70
600	8.25	10.50	7.20	9.93	6.46	9.49
650			8.35	10.75	7.49	10.29

* ASTM D2241.

Table B-23   PVC pipe—C=130—6 in. nominal diameter

| C = 130 | ID = Inside Diameter* | | | | | |
| | SDR14 ID = 5.796 | | SDR18 ID = 6.042 | | SDR25 ID = 6.282 | |
Flow, gpm	Head Loss, ft/100 ft	Velocity, ft/s	Head Loss, ft/100 ft	Velocity, ft/s	Head Loss, ft/100 ft	Velocity, ft/s
50	0.03	0.61	0.03	0.56	0.02	0.52
60	0.05	0.73	0.04	0.67	0.03	0.62
70	0.06	0.85	0.05	0.78	0.04	0.72
80	0.08	0.97	0.07	0.90	0.06	0.83
90	0.10	1.09	0.08	1.01	0.07	0.93
100	0.12	1.22	0.10	1.12	0.08	1.04
120	0.17	1.46	0.14	1.34	0.12	1.24
140	0.23	1.70	0.19	1.57	0.16	1.45
160	0.29	1.95	0.24	1.79	0.20	1.66
180	0.37	2.19	0.30	2.01	0.25	1.86
200	0.44	2.43	0.36	2.24	0.30	2.07
220	0.53	2.68	0.43	2.46	0.36	2.28
240	0.62	2.92	0.51	2.69	0.42	2.48
260	0.72	3.16	0.59	2.91	0.49	2.69
280	0.83	3.40	0.68	3.13	0.56	2.90
300	0.94	3.65	0.77	3.36	0.64	3.11
320	1.06	3.89	0.87	3.58	0.72	3.31
340	1.19	4.13	0.97	3.80	0.80	3.52
360	1.32	4.38	1.08	4.03	0.89	3.73
380	1.46	4.62	1.19	4.25	0.99	3.93
400	1.60	4.86	1.31	4.48	1.08	4.14
450	2.00	5.47	1.63	5.04	1.35	4.66
500	2.43	6.08	1.98	5.59	1.64	5.18
550	2.89	6.69	2.36	6.15	1.96	5.69
600	3.40	7.30	2.78	6.71	2.30	6.21
650	3.94	7.90	3.22	7.27	2.66	6.73
700	4.52	8.51	3.69	7.83	3.06	7.25
750	5.14	9.12	4.20	8.39	3.47	7.76
800	5.79	9.73	4.73	8.95	3.91	8.28

* AWWA C900.

(Table continued next page.)

Table B-23   PVC pipe—C=130—6 in. nominal diameter (continued)

| C = 130 | ID = Inside Diameter* | | | | | |
| | SDR14 ID = 5.796 | | SDR18 ID = 6.042 | | SDR25 ID = 6.282 | |
Flow, gpm	Head Loss, ft/100 ft	Velocity, ft/s	Head Loss, ft/100 ft	Velocity, ft/s	Head Loss, ft/100 ft	Velocity, ft/s
850	6.48	10.34	5.29	9.51	4.38	8.80
900			5.88	10.07	4.87	9.32
950					5.38	9.83
1000					5.92	10.35

* AWWA C900.

Table B-24   PVC pipe—C=130—8 in. nominal diameter

| C = 130 | ID = Inside Diameter* | | | | | |
| | SDR14 ID = 7.602 | | SDR18 ID = 7.924 | | SDR25 ID = 8.24 | |
Flow, gpm	Head Loss, ft/100 ft	Velocity, ft/s	Head Loss, ft/100 ft	Velocity, ft/s	Head Loss, ft/100 ft	Velocity, ft/s
130	0.05	0.92	0.04	0.85	0.04	0.78
140	0.06	0.99	0.05	0.91	0.04	0.84
150	0.07	1.06	0.06	0.98	0.05	0.90
160	0.08	1.13	0.06	1.04	0.05	0.96
170	0.09	1.20	0.07	1.11	0.06	1.02
180	0.10	1.27	0.08	1.17	0.07	1.08
190	0.11	1.34	0.09	1.24	0.07	1.14
200	0.12	1.41	0.10	1.30	0.08	1.20
220	0.14	1.56	0.12	1.43	0.10	1.32
240	0.17	1.70	0.14	1.56	0.11	1.44
260	0.19	1.84	0.16	1.69	0.13	1.56
280	0.22	1.98	0.18	1.82	0.15	1.68
300	0.25	2.12	0.21	1.95	0.17	1.80
350	0.33	2.47	0.27	2.28	0.23	2.11
400	0.43	2.83	0.35	2.60	0.29	2.41
450	0.53	3.18	0.44	2.93	0.36	2.71
500	0.65	3.53	0.53	3.25	0.44	3.01
550	0.77	3.89	0.63	3.58	0.52	3.31
600	0.91	4.24	0.74	3.90	0.61	3.61
650	1.05	4.59	0.86	4.23	0.71	3.91
700	1.21	4.95	0.99	4.55	0.82	4.21
750	1.37	5.30	1.12	4.88	0.93	4.51
800	1.55	5.65	1.26	5.20	1.04	4.81
850	1.73	6.01	1.41	5.53	1.17	5.11
900	1.92	6.36	1.57	5.86	1.30	5.41
950	2.12	6.72	1.74	6.18	1.43	5.72
1,000	2.34	7.07	1.91	6.51	1.58	6.02
1,100	2.79	7.78	2.28	7.16	1.88	6.62
1,200	3.27	8.48	2.68	7.81	2.21	7.22

* AWWA C900.

(Table continued next page.)

Table B-24 PVC pipe—*C*=130—8 in. nominal diameter (continued)

C = 130	ID = Inside Diameter*					
	SDR14 ID = 7.602		SDR18 ID = 7.924		SDR25 ID = 8.24	
Flow, *gpm*	Head Loss, *ft/100 ft*	Velocity, *ft/s*	Head Loss, *ft/100 ft*	Velocity, *ft/s*	Head Loss, *ft/100 ft*	Velocity, *ft/s*
1,300	3.80	9.19	3.10	8.46	2.57	7.82
1,400	4.36	9.90	3.56	9.11	2.94	8.42
1,500	4.95	10.60	4.04	9.76	3.34	9.02
1,600			4.56	10.41	3.77	9.63
1,700					4.22	10.23

* AWWA C900.

Table B-25 Polyethylene pipe (PE)—*C*=130—¾ in. nominal diameter

C = 130	ID = Inside Diameter*							
	Copper Tubing Sizes				Iron Pipe Sizes			
	DR9 ID = 0.681		DR 11 ID = 0.715		DR9 ID = 0.816		DR11 ID = 0.86	
Flow, *gpm*	Head Loss, *ft/100 ft*	Velocity, *ft/s*	Head Loss, *ft/100 ft*	Velocity, *ft/s*	Head Loss, *ft/100 ft*	Velocity, *ft/s*	Head Loss, *ft/100 ft*	Velocity, *ft/s*
1	0.82	0.88	0.65	0.80	0.34	0.61	0.26	0.55
2	2.98	1.76	2.35	1.60	1.23	1.23	0.95	1.10
3	6.30	2.64	4.97	2.40	2.61	1.84	2.02	1.66
4	10.74	3.52	8.47	3.20	4.45	2.45	3.45	2.21
5	16.24	4.40	12.81	4.00	6.73	3.07	5.21	2.76
6	22.76	5.29	17.95	4.79	9.43	3.68	7.30	3.31
7	30.27	6.17	23.88	5.59	12.55	4.29	9.72	3.87
8	38.77	7.05	30.58	6.39	16.07	4.91	12.44	4.42
9	48.22	7.93	38.03	7.19	19.98	5.52	15.47	4.97
10	58.60	8.81	46.22	7.99	24.29	6.13	18.81	5.52
11	69.92	9.69	55.15	8.79	28.98	6.75	22.44	6.08
12	82.14	10.57	64.79	9.59	34.04	7.36	26.36	6.63
13			75.14	10.39	39.48	7.98	30.57	7.18
14					45.29	8.59	35.07	7.73
15					51.46	9.20	39.85	8.28
16					57.99	9.82	44.91	8.84
17					64.89	10.43	50.24	9.39
18						0.61	55.85	9.94
19						1.23	61.73	10.49

* AWWA C901 (average outside diameter less minimum wall thickness).

Table B-26   PE pipe—C=130—1 in. nominal diameter

C = 130	ID = Inside Diameter*							
	Copper Tubing Sizes				Iron Pipe Sizes			
	DR9 ID = 0.875		DR11 ID = 0.921		DR9 ID = 1.023		DR11 ID = 1.077	
Flow, gpm	Head Loss, ft/100 ft	Velocity, ft/s	Head Loss, ft/100 ft	Velocity, ft/s	Head Loss, ft/100 ft	Velocity, ft/s	Head Loss, ft/100 ft	Velocity, ft/s
2	0.88	1.07	0.68	0.96	0.41	0.78	0.32	0.70
3	1.86	1.60	1.45	1.44	0.87	1.17	0.68	1.06
4	3.17	2.13	2.47	1.93	1.48	1.56	1.15	1.41
5	4.79	2.67	3.73	2.41	2.24	1.95	1.74	1.76
6	6.71	3.20	5.23	2.89	3.14	2.34	2.44	2.11
7	8.93	3.73	6.96	3.37	4.17	2.73	3.25	2.47
8	11.44	4.27	8.91	3.85	5.34	3.12	4.16	2.82
9	14.22	4.80	11.08	4.33	6.64	3.51	5.17	3.17
10	17.29	5.34	13.47	4.82	8.08	3.90	6.29	3.52
12	24.23	6.40	18.88	5.78	11.32	4.68	8.81	4.23
14	32.24	7.47	25.12	6.74	15.06	5.46	11.72	4.93
16	41.28	8.54	32.16	7.71	19.28	6.25	15.01	5.63
18	51.34	9.60	40.00	8.67	23.98	7.03	18.67	6.34
20			48.62	9.63	29.15	7.81	22.69	7.04
25					44.07	9.76	34.30	8.80
30							48.08	10.57

* AWWA C901 (average outside diameter less minimum wall thickness).

Table B-27   PE pipe—C=130—1¼ in. nominal diameter

C = 130	ID = Inside Diameter*							
	Copper Tubing Sizes				Iron Pipe Sizes			
	DR9 ID = 1.069		DR11 ID = 1.125		DR9 ID = 1.292		DR11 ID = 1.358	
Flow, gpm	Head Loss, ft/100 ft	Velocity, ft/s	Head Loss, ft/100 ft	Velocity, ft/s	Head Loss, ft/100 ft	Velocity, ft/s	Head Loss, ft/100 ft	Velocity, ft/s
5	1.81	1.79	1.41	1.61	0.72	1.22	0.56	1.11
6	2.53	2.14	1.97	1.94	1.01	1.47	0.79	1.33
7	3.37	2.50	2.63	2.26	1.34	1.71	1.05	1.55
8	4.31	2.86	3.36	2.58	1.71	1.96	1.34	1.77
9	5.36	3.22	4.18	2.90	2.13	2.20	1.67	1.99
10	6.52	3.57	5.08	3.23	2.59	2.45	2.03	2.22
12	9.14	4.29	7.13	3.87	3.63	2.94	2.85	2.66
15	13.81	5.36	10.77	4.84	5.49	3.67	4.31	3.32
20	23.53	7.15	18.35	6.46	9.35	4.89	7.34	4.43
25	35.57	8.94	27.74	8.07	14.14	6.12	11.09	5.54
30	49.86	10.72	38.88	9.68	19.81	7.34	15.54	6.65
35			51.72	11.30	26.36	8.57	20.68	7.75
40					33.75	9.79	26.48	8.86
45					41.98	11.01	32.94	9.97
50							40.03	11.08

* AWWA C901 (average outside diameter less minimum wall thickness).

Table B-28   PE pipe—C=130—1½ in. nominal diameter

C = 130	ID = Inside Diameter*							
	Copper Tubing Sizes				Iron Pipe Sizes			
	DR9 ID = 1.263		DR11 ID = 1.329		DR9 ID = 1.478		DR11 ID = 1.554	
Flow, gpm	Head Loss, ft/100 ft	Velocity, ft/s	Head Loss, ft/100 ft	Velocity, ft/s	Head Loss, ft/100 ft	Velocity, ft/s	Head Loss, ft/100 ft	Velocity, ft/s
8	1.91	2.05	1.49	1.85	0.89	1.50	0.70	1.35
9	2.38	2.30	1.86	2.08	1.11	1.68	0.87	1.52
10	2.89	2.56	2.26	2.31	1.35	1.87	1.05	1.69
12	4.06	3.07	3.16	2.78	1.89	2.24	1.48	2.03
15	6.13	3.84	4.78	3.47	2.85	2.80	2.23	2.54
20	10.44	5.12	8.15	4.63	4.86	3.74	3.80	3.38
25	15.79	6.40	12.32	5.78	7.34	4.67	5.75	4.23
30	22.13	7.68	17.27	6.94	10.29	5.61	8.06	5.07
35	29.44	8.96	22.97	8.09	13.69	6.54	10.72	5.92
40	37.70	10.24	29.42	9.25	17.53	7.48	13.73	6.77
45			36.59	10.41	21.81	8.41	17.08	7.61
50					26.50	9.35	20.76	8.46
55					31.62	10.28	24.77	9.30
60							29.10	10.15

* AWWA C901 (average outside diameter less minimum wall thickness).

Table B-29   PE pipe—C=130—2 in. nominal diameter

C = 130	ID = Inside Diameter*							
	Copper Tubing Sizes				Iron Pipe Sizes			
	DR9 ID = 1.653		DR11 ID = 1.739		DR9 ID = 1.847		DR11 ID = 1.943	
Flow, gpm	Head Loss, ft/100 ft	Velocity, ft/s	Head Loss, ft/100 ft	Velocity, ft/s	Head Loss, ft/100 ft	Velocity, ft/s	Head Loss, ft/100 ft	Velocity, ft/s
10	0.78	1.50	0.61	1.35	0.45	1.20	0.36	1.08
12	1.09	1.79	0.85	1.62	0.64	1.44	0.50	1.30
14	1.45	2.09	1.14	1.89	0.85	1.68	0.66	1.51
16	1.86	2.39	1.46	2.16	1.09	1.92	0.85	1.73
18	2.32	2.69	1.81	2.43	1.35	2.16	1.05	1.95
20	2.82	2.99	2.20	2.70	1.64	2.39	1.28	2.16
25	4.26	3.74	3.33	3.38	2.48	2.99	1.94	2.71
30	5.97	4.49	4.66	4.05	3.48	3.59	2.72	3.25
35	7.94	5.23	6.20	4.73	4.62	4.19	3.61	3.79
40	10.17	5.98	7.94	5.40	5.92	4.79	4.63	4.33
45	12.64	6.73	9.88	6.08	7.36	5.39	5.75	4.87
50	15.37	7.48	12.00	6.75	8.95	5.99	6.99	5.41
55	18.33	8.22	14.32	7.43	10.68	6.59	8.34	5.95
60	21.54	8.97	16.83	8.10	12.55	7.18	9.80	6.49
70	28.66	10.47	22.38	9.46	16.69	8.38	13.04	7.57
80			28.66	10.81	21.37	9.58	16.70	8.66
90					26.58	10.78	20.77	9.74
100							25.24	10.82

* AWWA C901 (average outside diameter less minimum wall thickness).

Table B-30 PE pipe—C=130—3 in. nominal diameter

C = 130	ID = Inside Diameter*							
	Copper Tubing Sizes				Iron Pipe Sizes			
	DR9 ID = N/A†		DR11 ID = N/A		DR9 ID = 2.722		DR11 ID = 2.864	
Flow, gpm	Head Loss, ft/100 ft	Velocity, ft/s	Head Loss, ft/100 ft	Velocity, ft/s	Head Loss, ft/100 ft	Velocity, ft/s	Head Loss, ft/100 ft	Velocity, ft/s
20	N/A	N/A	N/A	N/A	0.25	1.10	0.19	1.00
30	N/A	N/A	N/A	N/A	0.53	1.65	0.41	1.49
40	N/A	N/A	N/A	N/A	0.90	2.21	0.70	1.99
50	N/A	N/A	N/A	N/A	1.35	2.76	1.06	2.49
60	N/A	N/A	N/A	N/A	1.90	3.31	1.48	2.99
70	N/A	N/A	N/A	N/A	2.52	3.86	1.97	3.49
80	N/A	N/A	N/A	N/A	3.23	4.41	2.52	3.98
90	N/A	N/A	N/A	N/A	4.02	4.96	3.14	4.48
100	N/A	N/A	N/A	N/A	4.89	5.51	3.82	4.98
110	N/A	N/A	N/A	N/A	5.83	6.06	4.55	5.48
120	N/A	N/A	N/A	N/A	6.85	6.62	5.35	5.98
130	N/A	N/A	N/A	N/A	7.94	7.17	6.20	6.47
140	N/A	N/A	N/A	N/A	9.11	7.72	7.11	6.97
150	N/A	N/A	N/A	N/A	10.36	8.27	8.08	7.47
160			N/A	N/A	11.67	8.82	9.11	7.97
170			N/A	N/A	13.06	9.37	10.19	8.47
180					14.51	9.92	11.33	8.96
190					16.04	10.48	12.52	9.46
200							13.77	9.96
210							15.07	10.46

* AWWA C901 (average outside diameter less minimum wall thickness).

† NA= not applicable.

Table B-31 Cross-linked polyethylene (PEX) pipe—C=130— ½ in. nominal diameter, 0.625

C = 130	ID = Inside Diameter*		
	Copper Tubing Sizes		
	DR9 ID = 0.485		Thickness = 0.07
Flow, gpm	Head Loss, ft/100 ft	Velocity, ft/s	
1	4.31	1.74	
2	15.54	3.47	
3	32.93	5.21	
4	56.09	6.95	
5	84.80	8.68	
6	118.85	10.42	

* AWWA C904-06 (average outside diameter less minimum wall thickness).

Table B-32   PEX pipe—*C*=130—⅝ in. nominal diameter, 0.75+

C = 130	ID = Inside Diameter*		
	Copper Tubing Sizes		
	DR9 **ID = 0.583333**		Thickness = 0.083333
Flow, *gpm*	Head Loss, *ft/100 ft*	Velocity, *ft/s*	
1	1.75	1.20	
2	6.32	2.40	
3	13.40	3.60	
4	22.83	4.80	
5	34.51	6.00	
6	48.36	7.20	
7	64.34	8.40	
8	82.39	9.60	
9	102.48	10.80	

* AWWA C904-06 (average outside diameter less minimum wall thickness).

Table B-33   PEX pipe—*C*=130—¾ in. nominal diameter, 0.875

C = 130	ID = Inside Diameter*		
	Copper Tubing Sizes		
	DR9 **ID = 0.680556**		Thickness = 0.097222
Flow, *gpm*	Head Loss, *ft/100 ft*	Velocity, *ft/s*	
1	0.83	0.88	
2	2.98	1.76	
3	6.32	2.65	
4	10.77	3.53	
5	16.29	4.41	
6	22.83	5.29	
7	30.37	6.17	
8	38.89	7.06	
9	48.37	7.94	
10	58.79	8.82	
11	70.14	9.70	
12	82.40	10.58	

* AWWA C904-06 (average outside diameter less minimum wall thickness).

Table B-34   PEX pipe—*C*=130—1 in. nominal diameter, 1.125

C = 130	ID = Inside Diameter*		
	Copper Tubing Sizes		
	DR9 ID = 0.875		Thickness = 0.125
Flow, *gpm*	Head Loss, *ft/100 ft*	Velocity, *ft/s*	
1	0.24	0.53	
2	0.88	1.07	
3	1.86	1.60	
4	3.17	2.13	
5	4.79	2.67	
6	6.71	3.20	
7	8.93	3.73	
8	11.44	4.27	
9	14.22	4.80	
10	17.29	5.34	
11	20.62	5.87	
12	24.23	6.40	
13	28.10	6.94	
14	32.24	7.47	
15	36.63	8.00	
16	41.28	8.54	
17	46.18	9.07	
18	51.34	9.60	
19	56.75	10.14	

* AWWA C904-06 (average outside diameter less minimum wall thickness).

Table B-35   PEX pipe—*C*=130—1¼ in. nominal diameter, 1.375

C = 130	ID = Inside Diameter*		
	Copper Tubing Sizes		
	DR9 ID = 1.069444		Thickness = 0.152778
Flow, *gpm*	Head Loss, *ft/100 ft*	Velocity, *ft/s*	
1	0.09	0.36	
2	0.33	0.71	
3	0.70	1.07	
4	1.19	1.43	
5	1.80	1.79	
6	2.53	2.14	
7	3.36	2.50	
8	4.30	2.86	
9	5.35	3.21	
10	6.51	3.57	
11	7.76	3.93	
12	9.12	4.29	

* AWWA C904-06 (average outside diameter less minimum wall thickness).

(Table continued next page.)

Table B-35   PEX pipe—*C*=130—1¼ in. nominal diameter, 1.375 (continued)

C = 130	ID = Inside Diameter*		
	Copper Tubing Sizes		
	DR9 ID = 1.069444		Thickness = 0.152778
Flow, *gpm*	Head Loss, *ft/100 ft*	Velocity, *ft/s*	
13	10.58	4.64	
14	12.13	5.00	
15	13.78	5.36	
20	23.48	7.14	
25	35.50	8.93	
30	49.75	10.72	

* AWWA C904-06 (average outside diameter less minimum wall thickness).

Table B-36   PEX pipe—*C*=130—1½ in. nominal diameter, 1.625

C = 130	ID = Inside Diameter*		
	Copper Tubing Sizes		
	DR9 ID = 1.263889		Thickness = 0.180556
Flow, *gpm*	Head Loss, *ft/100 ft*	Velocity, *ft/s*	
1	0.04	0.26	
2	0.15	0.51	
3	0.31	0.77	
4	0.53	1.02	
5	0.80	1.28	
6	1.12	1.53	
7	1.49	1.79	
8	1.91	2.05	
9	2.37	2.30	
10	2.88	2.56	
11	3.44	2.81	
12	4.04	3.07	
13	4.69	3.32	
14	5.38	3.58	
15	6.11	3.84	
20	10.41	5.11	
25	15.73	6.39	
30	22.05	7.67	
35	29.34	8.95	
40	37.57	10.23	

* AWWA C904-06 (average outside diameter less minimum wall thickness).

Table B-37   PEX pipe—C=130—2 in. nominal diameter , 2.125

C = 130	ID = Inside Diameter*		
	Copper Tubing Sizes		
	DR9 ID = 1.652778		Thickness = 0.236111
Flow, *gpm*	Head Loss, *ft/100 ft*	Velocity, *ft/s*	
1	0.01	0.15	
2	0.04	0.30	
3	0.08	0.45	
4	0.14	0.60	
5	0.22	0.75	
10	0.78	1.50	
15	1.65	2.24	
20	2.82	2.99	
25	4.26	3.74	
30	5.97	4.49	
35	7.94	5.23	
40	10.17	5.98	
45	12.65	6.73	
50	15.38	7.48	
55	18.35	8.22	
60	21.55	8.97	
65	25.00	9.72	
70	28.67	10.47	

* AWWA C904-06 (average outside diameter less minimum wall thickness).

Table B-38   PEX pipe—C=130—2½ in. nominal diameter, 2.625

C = 130	ID = Inside Diameter*		
	Copper Tubing Sizes		
	DR9 ID = 2.041667		Thickness = 0.291667
Flow, *gpm*	Head Loss, *ft/100 ft*	Velocity, *ft/s*	
10	0.28	0.98	
15	0.59	1.47	
20	1.01	1.96	
25	1.52	2.45	
30	2.13	2.94	
35	2.84	3.43	
40	3.63	3.92	
45	4.52	4.41	
50	5.49	4.90	
55	6.56	5.39	
60	7.70	5.88	
65	8.93	6.37	
70	10.25	6.86	

* AWWA C904-06 (average outside diameter less minimum wall thickness).

(Table continued next page.)

Table B-38   PEX pipe—*C*=130—2½ in. nominal diameter, 2.625 (continued)

C = 130	ID = Inside Diameter*		
	Copper Tubing Sizes		
	DR9 ID = 2.041667		Thickness = 0.291667
Flow, *gpm*	Head Loss, *ft/100 ft*	Velocity, *ft/s*	
75	11.64	7.35	
80	13.12	7.84	
85	14.68	8.33	
90	16.32	8.82	
95	18.04	9.31	
100	19.83	9.80	
105	21.71	10.29	

* AWWA C904-06 (average outside diameter less minimum wall thickness).

Table B-39   PEX pipe—*C*=130—3 in. nominal diameter, 3.125

C = 130	ID = Inside Diameter*		
	Copper Tubing Sizes		
	DR9 ID = 2.430556		Thickness = 0.347222
Flow, *gpm*	Head Loss, *ft/100 ft*	Velocity, *ft/s*	
50	2.35	3.46	
55	2.80	3.80	
60	3.29	4.15	
65	3.82	4.49	
70	4.38	4.84	
75	4.98	5.19	
80	5.61	5.53	
85	6.28	5.88	
90	6.98	6.22	
95	7.72	6.57	
100	8.48	6.91	
105	9.29	7.26	
110	10.12	7.61	
115	10.99	7.95	
120	11.89	8.30	
125	12.83	8.64	
130	13.79	8.99	
135	14.79	9.33	
140	15.82	9.68	
145	16.88	10.03	

* AWWA C904-06 (average outside diameter less minimum wall thickness).

This page intentionally blank.

Index

NOTE: *f.* indicates figure; *t.* indicates table.

AWWA Manuals

M1, *Principles of Water Rates, Fees, and Charges,* #30001

M2, *Instrumentation and Control,* #30002

M3, *Safety Management for Water Utilities,* #30003

M4, *Water Fluoridation Principles and Practices,* #30004

M5, *Water Utility Management,* #30005

M6, *Water Meters—Selection, Installation, Testing, and Maintenance,* #30006

M7, *Problem Organisms in Water: Identification and Treatment,* #30007

M9, *Concrete Pressure Pipe,* #30009

M11, *Steel Pipe—A Guide for Design and Installation,* #30011

M12, *Simplified Procedures for Water Examination,* #30012

M14, *Backflow Prevention and Cross-Connection Control,* #30014

M17, *Installation, Field Testing, and Maintenance of Fire Hydrants,* #30017

M19, *Emergency Planning for Water Utilities,* #30019

M20, *Water Chlorination/Chloramination Practices and Principles,* #30020

M21, *Groundwater,* #30021

M22, *Sizing Water Service Lines and Meters,* #30022

M23, *PVC Pipe—Design and Installation,* #30023

M24, *Planning for the Distribution of Reclaimed Water,* #30024

M25, *Flexible-Membrane Covers and Linings for Potable-Water Reservoirs,* #30025

M27, *External Corrosion Control for Infrastructure Sustainability,* #30027

M28, *Rehabilitation of Water Mains,* #30028

M29, *Water Utility Capital Financing,* #30029

M30, *Precoat Filtration,* #30030

M31, *Distribution System Requirements for Fire Protection,* #30031

M32, *Computer Modeling of Water Distribution Systems,* #30032

M33, *Flowmeters in Water Supply,* #30033

M36, *Water Audits and Loss Control Programs,* #30036

M37, *Operational Control of Coagulation and Filtration Processes,* #30037

M38, *Electrodialysis and Electrodialysis Reversal,* #30038

M41, *Ductile-Iron Pipe and Fittings,* #30041

M42, *Steel Water-Storage Tanks,* #30042

M44, *Distribution Valves: Selection, Installation, Field Testing, and Maintenance,* #30044

M45, *Fiberglass Pipe Design,* #30045

M46, *Reverse Osmosis and Nanofiltration,* #30046

M47, *Capital Project Delivery,* #30047

M48, *Waterborne Pathogens,* #30048

M49, *Butterfly Valves: Torque, Head Loss, and Cavitation Analysis,* #30049

M50, *Water Resources Planning,* #30050

M51, *Air-Release, Air/Vacuum, and Combination Air Valves,* #30051

M52, *Water Conservation Programs—A Planning Manual,* #30052

M53, *Microfiltration and Ultrafiltration Membranes for Drinking Water,* #30053

M54, *Developing Rates for Small Systems,* #30054

M55, *PE Pipe—Design and Installation,* #30055

M56, *Nitrification Prevention and Control in Drinking Water,* #30056

M57, *Algae: Source to Treatment,* #30057

M58, *Internal Corrosion Control in Water Distribution Systems,* #30058

M60, *Drought Preparedness and Response,* #30060

M61, *Desalination of Seawater,* #30061

This page intentionally blank.